Raintree Steck-Vaughn

Illustrated
SCIENCE
ENCYCLOPEDIA

Volume
12

LEE – MAR

RSVP

**RAINTREE
STECK-VAUGHN**
P U B L I S H E R S
The Steck-Vaughn Company

Austin, Texas

Published by Raintree Steck-Vaughn Publishers, an imprint of
Steck-Vaughn Company.

Executive Editor	Diane Sharpe
Senior Editor	Anne Souby
Design Manager	Joyce Spicer

This edition edited and designed by Andromeda Oxford Ltd.

Andromeda Editorial and Design

Project Manager	Julia Roles
Editorial Manager	Jenny Fry
Design	TT Designs, T&S Truscott
Cover Design	John Barker

Library of Congress Cataloging-in-Publication Data
Raintree Steck-Vaughn illustrated science encyclopedia.
        p.   cm.
    Includes bibliographical references and index.
    Summary: A twenty-four volume set containing brief articles
on science topics.
    ISBN 0-8172-3943-X (set)
    ISBN 0-8172-3930-8 (Volume 12)
    1. Science—Encyclopedias, Juvenile.   [1. Science—
Encyclopedias.]   I. Raintree Steck-Vaughn Publishers.
Q121.R354   1997
503—dc20   96-11078
                                                  CIP
                                                    AC

Printed and Bound in the United States of America.
1 2 3 4 5 6 7 8 9 10 IP 00 99 98 97 96

USING THE RAINTREE STECK-VAUGHN ILLUSTRATED SCIENCE ENCYCLOPEDIA

You are living in a world in which science, technology, and nature are very important. You see something about science almost every day. It might be on television, in the newspaper, in a book at school, or some other place. Often, you want more information about what you see.

The *Raintree Steck-Vaughn Illustrated Science Encyclopedia* will help you find what you want to know. It contains information on many science subjects. You may want to find out about computers, the environment, space exploration, biology, agriculture, or mathematics, for example. They are all in the *Raintree Steck-Vaughn Illustrated Science Encyclopedia*. There are many, many other subjects covered as well.

There are twenty-four volumes in the encyclopedia. The articles, which are called entries, are in alphabetical order through the first twenty-two volumes. On the spine of each volume, below the volume number, are some letters. The letters above the line are the first three letters of the first entry in that volume. The letters below the line are the first three letters of the last entry in that volume. In Volume 1, for example, you see that the first entry begins with **AAR** and that the last entry begins with **ANT**. Using the letters makes it easy to find the volume you need.

In Volume 23, there are three special features—reference charts and tables, a bibliography, and an index. In Volume 24, there are interesting projects that you can do on your own. The projects are fun to do, and they help you discover and understand important science principles. Many can give you ideas that can help you develop your own science fair projects.

Main Entries There are two kinds of main entries in the *Raintree Steck-Vaughn Illustrated Science Encyclopedia*. Many of the entries are major topics that are spread over several pages. The titles of these entries are shown at the top of the page in a yellow box. Other entries required less space to cover the topic fully. The titles of these main entries are printed in capital letters. They look like this: **ABALONE**. At the beginning of some entries, you will see a phonetic pronunciation of the entry title, such as (ăb´ ə lō´ nē).

In the front of each volume, there is a pronunciation key. Use it the same way you use your dictionary's pronunciation key.

Cross-References Within the main entries are cross-references referring to other entries in the encyclopedia. Within an entry, they look like this: (see MAMMAL). At the end of an entry, they look like this: *See also* HYENA. These cross-references tell you where to find other helpful information on the subject you are reading about.

Projects At the end of some entries, you will see this symbol: ⚡ PROJECT 1. It tells you which projects related to that entry are in Volume 24.

Illustrations There are thousands of photographs, drawings, graphs, diagrams, tables, and other illustrations in the *Raintree Steck-Vaughn Illustrated Science Encyclopedia*. They will help you better understand the entries you read. Captions describe the illustrations. Many of the illustrations also have labels that point out important parts.

Activities Some main entries include activities presented in a special box. These activities are short projects that give you a chance to work with science on your own.

Index In Volume 23, the index lists every main entry by volume and page number. Many subjects that are not main entries are also listed in the index, as well as the illustrations, projects, activities, and reference charts and tables.

Bibliography In Volume 23, there is also a bibliography for students. The books in this list are on a variety of topics and can supplement what you have learned in the *Raintree Steck-Vaughn Illustrated Science Encyclopedia*.

The *Raintree Steck-Vaughn Illustrated Science Encyclopedia* was designed especially for you, the student. It is a source of knowledge for the world of science, technology, and nature. Enjoy it!

PRONUNCIATION KEY

Each symbol has the same sound as the darker letters in the sample words.

ə	balloon, ago	îr	deer, pier	r	root, tire
ă	map, have	j	join, germ	s	so, press
ā	day, made	k	king, ask	sh	shoot, machine
âr	care, bear	l	let, cool	t	to, stand
ä	father, car	m	man, same	th	thin, death
b	ball, rib	n	no, turn	*th*	then, this
ch	choose, nature	ng	bring, long	ŭ	up, cut
d	did, add	ŏ	odd, pot	ûr	urge, hurt
ĕ	bell, get	ō	cone, know	v	view, give
ē	sweet, easy	ô	all, saw	w	wood, glowing
f	fan, soft	oi	boy, boil	y	yes, year
g	good, big	ou	now, loud	z	zero, raise
h	hurt, ahead	o͝o	good, took	zh	leisure, vision
ĭ	rip, ill	o͞o	boot, noon	'	strong accent
ī	side, sky	p	part, scrap	ˊ	weak accent

GUIDE TO MEASUREMENT ABBREVIATIONS

All measurements in the *Raintree Steck-Vaughn Illustrated Science Encyclopedia* are given in both the customary system and the metric system [in brackets like these]. Following are the abbreviations used for various units of measure.

Customary Units of Measure

mi. = miles	cu. yd. = cubic yards
m.p.h. = miles per hour	cu. ft. = cubic feet
yd. = yards	cu. in. = cubic inches
ft. = feet	gal. = gallons
in. = inches	pt. = pints
sq. mi. = square miles	qt. = quarts
sq. yd. = square yards	lb. = pounds
sq. ft. = square feet	oz. = ounces
sq. in. = square inches	fl. oz. = fluid ounces
cu. mi. = cubic miles	°F = degrees Fahrenheit

Metric Units of Measure

km = kilometers	cu. km = cubic kilometers
kph = kilometers per hour	cu. m = cubic meters
m = meters	cu. cm = cubic centimeters
cm = centimeters	ml = milliliters
mm = millimeters	kg = kilograms
sq. km = square kilometers	g = grams
sq. m = square meters	mg = milligrams
sq. cm = square centimeters	°C = degrees Celsius

For information on how to convert customary measurements to metric measurements, see the Metric Conversions table in Volume 23.

LEECH A leech is a worm belonging to the phylum Annelida (see ANNELIDA). There are over 300 species and most of them live in fresh water. Some live in damp places on land and a few live in the sea. The leech has a sucker at each end, although the one around the mouth is often quite small. The animal moves by anchoring the rear sucker and stretching forward, and then anchoring the front and pulling up the rear. Water-dwelling species can also swim with graceful snakelike movements. Most leeches eat small aquatic creatures, both living and dead, but some are bloodsuckers and will feed on blood from any animal they can find, including human beings. The medicinal leech, which is up to 6 in. [15 cm] long, was regularly used by European doctors in the past to draw blood from sick people. It was believed that the leeches would suck out the "bad blood" that was causing the illness. The practice was abandoned for a long time, but leeches are now being used again because the saliva that they inject while feeding contains a substance that helps to thin the blood. This can be helpful in treating some illnesses.

LEECH
The freshwater leech (above) has many of its young attached to its skin. Leeches move by extending their front ends, gripping the surface with the sucker-mouth, and pulling up their rear ends (below).

LEEK Leek is a hardy, biennial plant belonging to the lily family (see BIENNIAL PLANT; LILY FAMILY). It is similar to the onion and garlic plants, but its flavor is much milder. This vegetable grows from a seed and produces an elongated bulb that is thick with stored food (see BULB AND CORM). The plant is usually harvested at the end of its first growing season for its bulb and leaves. These are used as a flavoring for soups and stews, or boiled and served like asparagus. Leeks have been cultivated for thousands of years in the Mediterranean area.

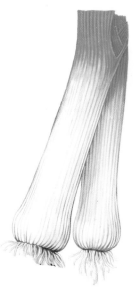

LEEK
Leeks are usuallly planted fairly deep in the soil (above left). This lengthens the white, edible part of the stem (above right).

LEEUWENHOEK, ANTON VAN (1632–1723) (lā′ vən hōōk′, än′tôn vän) Anton van Leeuwenhoek was a naturalist. He was born in Delft, Holland. He made more than two hundred microscopes to use in his studies. Van Leeuwenhoek's microscopes had only one lens. Microscopes with two lenses at that time gave colored, fuzzy edges to objects being examined. Two-lens microscopes were not significantly improved until more than a hundred years after van

Leeuwenhoek died. His tiny, very thick lenses were so good, however, that they could make things look more than two hundred times larger.

With his microscopes, van Leeuwenhoek discovered red blood cells, sperm cells, yeast cells, and protozoans. In 1683, he looked at scrapings from between his teeth and was the first person to see bacteria. He described them as "minute [tiny] rods, which show movement" and called them flora (flowers) of the mouth.

See also BACTERIA; LENS; MICROSCOPE.

LEGIONNAIRES' DISEASE Legionnaires' disease is a form of pneumonia that was first identified in 1976 (see PNEUMONIA). Over 200 delegates attending an American Legion meeting in Philadelphia and staying at the same hotel became ill with pneumonia and 29 died. Scientists with the Centers for Disease Control and Prevention in Georgia discovered that the organism causing the pneumonia had many unique properties and was unlike any other bacterium then known. They called the bacterium *Legionella pneumophila*. It grows slowly and only in moist conditions, and is not stained by the usual stains used to examine samples for pneumonia-causing organisms. It can also survive for up to a year in tap water.

The symptoms of Legionnaires' disease are a general feeling of weakness, headache, then a high fever. Coughing, shortness of breath, and pain in the lungs occur, with the development of pneumonia, which can be fatal. The disease is not spread by person-to-person contact, but through infected water supplies or through contaminated air-conditioning systems. Treatment is with antibiotics.

LEGUME (lĕg′ yōōm′) A legume is the fruit of plants of the pea family. When the fruit is ripe, it splits open along two seams to release seeds. Legumes are sometimes called pods. The word *legume* is also used to refer to any plant of the pea family, which used to be called the Leguminosae but is now generally called the Fabaceae.

See also DEHISCENCE; DISPERSION OF PLANTS; FRUIT; PEA FAMILY.

LEGUME

Broad beans, seen in bloom (top), are among the many types of legumes that are grown for their edible pods and seeds. Red beans (bottom) are left to dry in the sun. They can then be stored for many months.

LEMMING The lemming is a small, plump rodent belonging to the family Cricetidae (see RODENT). Lemmings grow from 4 to 6.5 in. [10 to 16.5 cm] long, including their stubby tails. Most lemmings have grayish or brownish fur. They feed on plants and live in nests dug in the soil, which they line with grass and moss.

Lemmings live in the cold northern parts of the world. The best-known kind lives in the Scandinavian countries, such as Norway. A story says that every year, hundreds of thousands of Scandinavian lemmings march to the sea in a long, packed line. There, the story goes, they leap into the ocean and drown. Because of this legend, the word *lemming* has come to mean a person who follows another person, or persons, without thinking.

Scientists have proved that the legend is not true. Their studies have shown that lemmings do move away from their homes in large groups because of overpopulation. Some lemmings do drown when they try to cross rivers and canals. However, they do not drown themselves on purpose.

LEMUR
All lemurs have long, bushy tails. Pictured here are the gray gentle lemur (left) and the ring-tailed lemur (below).

LEMMING
The Norway lemming (above) is more colorful than most lemming species.

LEMUR (lē′ mər) Lemurs are long-tailed mammals belonging to the primate order (see MAMMAL; PRIMATE). Some kinds of lemurs look like monkeys. Others look like squirrels, and some are as small as mice. Lemurs are found only in Madagascar and Comoros. These are islands off the southeast coast of Africa.

Lemurs live mostly in trees. They feed mainly on fruits, leaves, birds, and insects. Some kinds of lemurs are active at night. Others move about during the day.

The most common species, the ring-tailed lemur, looks like a monkey, except it has a long, pointed snout. The ring-tailed lemur grows to about 4 ft. [120 cm] in length, but over half of this length is the tail. It has a gray back, and black and white rings on its tail.

Lemurs have few enemies. There are few large predators (animals that eat other animals) in Madagascar and Comoros. However, many species of lemurs are in danger because the forests in which they live are being cut down.
See also ENDANGERED SPECIES.

LENS A lens is a specially shaped piece of transparent material used to bend rays of light. Lenses are usually made of glass or plastic. They work by refraction (the bending of light rays) (see LIGHT; REFRACTION OF LIGHT). Light rays change direction when they enter the lens and again when they leave it. The surfaces of the lens are curved. The curves are arranged so that wherever light strikes the lens, the rays are bent in the desired direction. In this way, light can be brought to one point, or focus. It can also be directed to form a parallel beam of light. There are many designs of lenses for different purposes.

Lenses and images Most lenses are designed to focus light to form images, or pictures of objects. The lens of a camera forms an image that can be

LENS—Eyeglasses

A common use of lenses is in eyeglasses. (1) The lens in a normal eye focuses an image on the retina. (2) The eye of a person who is farsighted needs a convex lens to correct the focus. (3) The eye of a person who is nearsighted needs a concave lens.

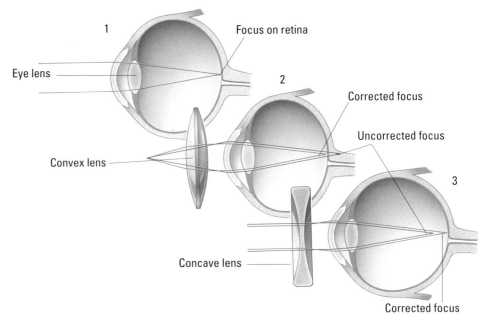

LENS—Camera lens

Many modern cameras have interchangeable lenses. The photographer can choose a lens that has the right focal length for the subject being photographed.

captured on film. The lens of the eye forms an image on the retina at the back of the eyeball. Microscope lenses form greatly magnified images of small objects (see CAMERA; EYE AND VISION; MICROSCOPE).

The faces of a lens can be curved in different ways. A surface that bulges outward is convex. One that is scooped out is concave (see CONCAVE; CONVEX). When both faces of a lens are convex, light rays passing through are made to converge, or come together. They form an image that can be shown on a suitable screen. This kind of lens is called a positive or converging lens, and the image is a real image. The image is on the opposite side of the lens from the object.

If both sides of a lens are concave, the lens is called a negative or diverging lens. It makes light rays diverge, or move apart, as they pass through. Looking through the lens, one can see an image of objects on the other side. However, it is not an image that can be projected on a screen. It is a virtual image. It is the same kind of image as one sees when looking in a mirror, but smaller.

Simple lenses usually have faces that are identical. For more complicated uses, as in optical instruments and eyeglasses, the two faces may have quite different curvatures.

Focusing When parallel light rays are bent by a positive lens, they meet at the principal focus of the lens. At this point, the image is clearest and sharpest for very distant objects. Rays from these objects are very nearly parallel. The distance from the lens to the principal focus is called the focal length of the lens. The lens of a camera is placed at its focal length from the photographic film. This brings distant objects into clear focus. However, light rays from near objects are not parallel when they strike the lens. They therefore meet at a different focus than the principal focus. The lens must then be moved, or focused, to make the image of near objects clear and sharp on the film.

In the human eye, focusing is brought about by muscles that alter the shape of the lens. It can be pulled thinner or allowed to bulge. The fatter the lens is, the shorter the focal length.

Lens defects A simple lens refracts different wavelengths of light to different extents. This is why a prism is able to split white light into different colors (see PRISM; SPECTRUM). The image formed by a simple lens is surrounded by a spectrum of colored fringes because of this. This defect is called chromatic (color) aberration (see ABERRATION).

Another form of defect is called spherical aberration. This occurs because rays that pass nearly through the center of the lens focus at a slightly different distance than rays that pass through the edges of the lens. Not all of the object is focused at the same distance. The image becomes blurred.

Both of these defects can be corrected. They are corrected by making compound lenses. Compound lenses are made of several pieces of glass fitted together. They are made of glass with different densities. They refract light slightly differently and cancel out the defects. A simple means of correcting chromatic aberration is to use a positive lens together with a negative lens of a different kind of glass. This forms an achromatic lens. *Achromatic* means "color-free."

Uses of lenses Lenses are used in many different ways. They are used in eyeglasses and as contact lenses to make up for poor vision. Simple lenses are used in magnifying glasses to produce enlarged images. Complex arrangements of lenses are used in telescopes and microscopes, cameras, motion-picture projectors, and all optical instruments. Huge lenses are used in searchlights and lighthouses.

See also MAGNIFICATION; PHOTOGRAPHY; TELESCOPE. PROJECT 27, 41

LENTIL The lentil is a plant belonging to the pea family (see PEA FAMILY). It reaches a height of 18 in. [45 cm] and has tendrils, or stems, for support (see TENDRIL). It has alternate leaves made up of four to seven pairs of leaflets, and pale blue or white flowers (see LEAF). The flowers produce legumes or pods that are about 0.6 in. [15 mm] long (see LEGUME). Each legume has one or two small, flat seeds, which are also called lentils. These lentils may be reddish

LENTIL
The short pods of lentils (top) hold only one or two seeds, which are gathered and dried. The dried seeds (above) can then be used in cooking.

brown, black, green, or gray. They are high in protein and carbohydrates, and are used in salads, soups, and casseroles.

LENZ'S LAW Lenz's law helps explain electromagnetism. When a conductor of electricity is moved in a magnetic field, a current will start to flow in it. This is called induction. The force that drives the electric current is called an induced electromotive force, and the current is an induced current. Lenz's law states that when an electromotive force and current are induced this way, they act to oppose the movement of the conductor. They do this by inducing their own magnetic field, opposing the existing one. The Russian physicist Heinrich Lenz announced this law in 1834.

See also ELECTROMAGNETISM.

LEONARDO DA VINCI

Leonardo da Vinci was an artist, scientist, and inventor. This picture is based on a self-portrait.

LEONARDO DA VINCI (1452–1519)

(lē´ə när´ dō də vĭn´ chē) Leonardo da Vinci was an Italian artist. His paintings and sculptures are famous. He studied anatomy—the body and its parts—to help him with his art. He dissected (cut up) and drew the corpses of humans as well as horses. His drawings are very accurate. He observed and drew certain parts of the body that people did not yet understand. However, his wonderful powers of observation helped him draw exactly what was there. His drawings also show his skill in dissection and analysis of the human body.

Leonardo also made drawings of machines that did not yet exist. At a time when people had only horses and sailboats to help them move from place to place, he drew plans for flying machines. He even experimented with building these machines. He also drew plans for diving bells, underground canals, and war machinery.

However, Leonardo da Vinci did not really have much to do with the growth of technology. Very few people knew of his inventions. It is only because he carefully preserved all his drawings that we know so much about his ideas.

LEOPARD The leopard is a large member of the cat family. In the Eastern Hemisphere, only the lion and tiger are larger. Leopards are found in Africa and Asia.

Leopards are graceful and alert. They are about 2 ft. 4 in. [71 cm] high at the shoulder, and 7 ft. 6 in. [2.3 m] in length, including the tail. The leopard's coat is usually yellow to tan, with many black spots on it. Some leopards are so dark that the spots are hard to see. Albinos that are very pale and without much color are rare.

Leopards feed mainly on monkeys, antelopes, jackals, peacocks, snakes, sheep, goats, and wild dogs. Leopards seldom attack human beings.

Leopards are good climbers. They spend some of their time in trees. The animals are very strong. Leopards often carry bodies of prey weighing 80 to 150 lb. [36 to 68 kg] up into trees. This keeps the leopard's meal from being taken by lions or hyenas.

Because they have been hunted for their fur, leopards have become very rare in many places. Several

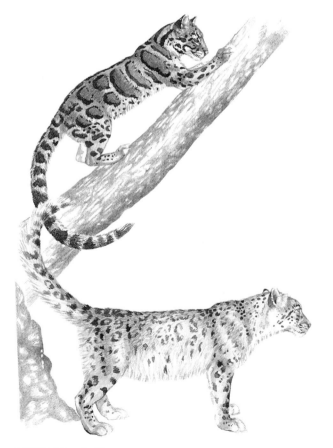

LEOPARD—Different types

Leopards are good climbers. Pictured here are the clouded leopard (top) and the snow leopard.

Flashlight photography has caught this leopard waiting for crocodiles to be fed at a river in a game reserve in Kenya. The leopard will then try to steal food from the crocodiles.

subspecies are in danger of disappearing. The United States and certain other countries no longer allow leopard skins to be imported.

See also CAT; ENDANGERED SPECIES.

LEPROSY Leprosy is a crippling infectious disease of the skin and peripheral nerves (see DISEASE; NERVOUS SYSTEM). Leprosy occurs most often in tropical areas. However, it also affects people in Korea, central Mexico, and, occasionally, in some of the southern states of the United States. It is a disease that develops slowly. Although it is an infectious disease that is transmitted from person to person, it is not as easily spread as was once thought.

Leprosy is caused by bacteria (*Mycobacterium leprae*) similar to the bacteria that cause tuberculosis (see TUBERCULOSIS). The bacteria are found in the skin and nerves. They cause lumps and patches of discoloration in the skin of the ears, the face, and the limbs. The inside surfaces of the mouth and nose also may be affected. When the disease spreads to the eyes, it can cause blindness. Nerves that are attacked by leprosy are destroyed. The fingers and toes, as well as patches of infected skin, may lose all feeling. The hands and feet may become weakened and even paralyzed.

Leprosy can be cured with modern drugs. The drug dapsone belongs to a group of chemicals known as sulfones and is particularly effective. Other drugs used are rifampin and clofazimine. The sulfones are fairly inexpensive. This is important because great numbers of patients in poor countries need to be treated. Early treatment can stop the disease, and most patients can be helped. People who are badly crippled and disfigured may also need surgery and physical therapy. The World Health Organization, UNICEF, and other international organizations are engaged in a continuous worldwide fight against leprosy.

LESSEPS, FERDINAND DE (1805–1894) Ferdinand de Lesseps was a French diplomat and engineer. He was a man of great energy. While he was a diplomat, he spent some time in Egypt. In 1832, he had an idea for a canal across the Suez isthmus, a strip of land running along the northern edge of the Red Sea. The canal would link the Red and Mediterranean seas. Later, he quit the diplomatic service and went back to Egypt. He began planning the Suez Canal in 1854. Work began on the canal in 1859. It was opened ten years later. De Lesseps received many honors and awards for his work on the canal.

In 1879, he began work on an even greater plan. This was the Panama Canal, to run through Central America, linking the Atlantic and Pacific oceans. However, he had too difficult a plan. He wanted to make the canal at sea level without any locks. The work was very hard, and many people died of illness and accidents. After eight years' work, only one-quarter of the canal had been dug. De Lesseps's company went out of business in 1888. He was disgraced and sentenced to five years in prison in 1893. He was released that same year because he was very old and sick. He died a year later.

See also LOCK (NAVIGATIONAL).

LETTUCE Lettuce is a popular salad vegetable belonging to the composite family (see COMPOSITE FAMILY). It is cultivated in temperate areas all over the world. Lettuce is a good source of fiber in the diet, and it also provides vitamins and minerals (see DIET). The plant has large, green leaves, and grows close to the ground on a short stem. Most of the numerous cultivated varieties form dense heads of leaves.

There are many varieties of lettuce. Some include asparagus lettuce, head lettuce, leaf lettuce, and romaine lettuce. Asparagus lettuce has narrow leaves and a thick stem that can be eaten. Head lettuce has leaves curled into a ball-shaped head. Crisp head lettuce (iceberg lettuce) has brittle, juicy leaves packed in a dense head. Butterhead lettuce has a looser head made of thick, oily leaves. Leaf lettuce has leaves arranged in dense clumps instead of in heads. Romaine lettuce has loose heads of tall, rectangular leaves.

LETTUCE
Lettuce varieties range from loose, curly-leaved types to those with dense, whitish heads.

LEUCOCYTE (lōō′ kə sīt′) *Leucocyte* is the scientific name for a white blood cell. Leucocytes help protect the body against infectious diseases. Leucocytes are formed mainly in bone marrow.

Leucocytes move through the body in the blood. One type of leucocyte, called a neutrophil, fights bacterial infections by consuming bacteria.

Another type of leucocyte, called a lymphocyte, helps prevent disease by producing antibodies. Antibodies are proteins that help destroy pathogens (disease-causing organisms). The ability to produce specific antibodies quickly may continue even after the pathogen has been destroyed. If this happens, the body has become immune to that pathogen. Antibodies that destroy poisons are called antitoxins. A third type of leucocyte, called a monocyte, works with neutrophils to consume bacteria and works with lymphocytes during immune reactions. *See also* ANTIBODY; BLOOD; DISEASE; IMMUNITY; INFECTION; PATHOGEN.

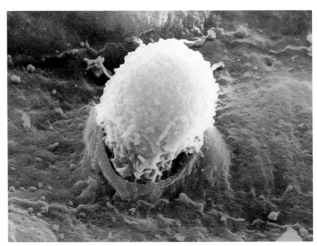

LEUCOCYTE
A leucocyte is a white blood cell. Here, a leucocyte passes through the wall of a blood vessel into the surrounding tissue, where it will help the body's defenses fight disease.

LEUKEMIA (lōō kē′ mē ə) Leukemia is a form of cancer involving the blood-forming tissues of the body. In normal blood, there are great numbers of red blood cells and a much smaller number of white blood cells. The red blood cells carry oxygen to all tissues of the body. The white blood cells are an important part of the immune system, which defends the body against bacteria and viruses (see BLOOD; IMMUNITY). White blood cells are produced mainly in the bone marrow and are found in large numbers in the lymph nodes (see LYMPHATIC SYSTEM). In leukemia, something goes wrong with the tissues that produce white blood cells. Great numbers of white blood cells are produced. A person with leukemia may have thirty to sixty times the normal number of white blood cells a healthy person has. At the same time, fewer red blood cells are formed. The person, therefore, also suffers from anemia (see ANEMIA).

In leukemia, the rate of production of white cells becomes completely uncontrolled. At the same time, the white cells are abnormal. Although there are many white blood cells, they are of no use. The person is very liable to infection, and there may be hemorrhage (bleeding) from the nose and gums and into internal organs because fewer platelets, which also are produced by the bone marrow, are present. The lymph nodes and spleen may become swollen with all the extra white blood cells (see SPLEEN). There may be other symptoms, such as pain in the bones and fever.

There are various kinds of leukemia, classified according to which type of abnormal white blood cell is present, the proportion of abnormal cells in the blood, and whether the disease occurred suddenly (acute leukemia) or developed slowly (chronic leukemia). With treatment, patients may survive for many years. Drugs can be given to destroy the abnormal cells, and patients may be treated with X rays and radioactive isotopes (see RADIATION THERAPY). Blood transfusions may also be given. New therapy with bone marrow transplantation has offered a

chance of cure for some people with leukemia. However, at this time, the disease is usually fatal.

It is known that leukemia can be caused by exposure to a certain kind of radiation (like that which occurred after the atomic bombing of Japan during World War II); certain viruses; some chemicals (known as alkylating agents); and genetic tendency. An identical twin of a child with acute leukemia has a 20 percent chance of also developing the disease. *See also* CANCER; HEREDITY.

LEVEE A levee is a wall built along the banks of a river to stop flooding. Levees have held back the waters of the southern Mississippi River for many years. In 1718, a small levee was built at New Orleans to stop the flooding of a small piece of farmland. Since the late 1800s, the U.S. government has helped build many levees along the Mississippi. The world's largest system of levees, covering a total of 3,566 mi. [5,739 km], is constructed along the Mississippi River and its tributaries. Most of the levees are built out of earth and

LEVEE

Levees are walls built alongside rivers. They prevent the rivers from flooding. Shown here is the Mississippi River and levee near Convent in Louisiana.

sandbags. They range in height from 15 to 30 ft. [4.6 to 9.1 m]. They are 8 ft. [2.4 m] wide at the top, increasing to 100 ft. [30 m] at the base.

There is some worry about levees. Levees allow the water to flow at a higher level than it otherwise would. If a levee were to break, great flooding might take place. Therefore, rules have been made about the heights of levees.

See also DAM; DIKE.

LEVER A lever is a rigid bar that can turn around a pivot or support, called a fulcrum (see FULCRUM). A lever is a simple machine (see MACHINE, SIMPLE). It can be used to do work (to move a load) (see LOAD). Effort is applied to one part of the lever. The lever pushes a load at another part. Usually the effort is smaller than the load, so the lever makes it easier to move the load.

There are three kinds of levers. A first-class lever has the effort and the load on either side of the fulcrum. A crowbar and a seesaw are examples of first-class levers. If the load is closer to the fulcrum than to the effort, a first-class lever acts as a force magnifier, allowing a small effort to move a larger load. The lever is said to have a mechanical

advantage greater than one. If the effort is closer to the fulcrum than to the load, the effort must be larger than the load. The mechanical advantage is less than one. In this case, the lever acts as a movement magnifier. The load moves a greater distance than the effort.

A second-class lever has the load between the fulcrum and the effort. An example is a nutcracker or a wheelbarrow. A second-class lever always acts as a force magnifier. Its mechanical advantage is always greater than one. A third-class lever has the effort between the load and the fulcrum. An example is a

LEVER

Pictured here are the three classes of levers, with examples of their use below them. They differ in the positions of the load and effort in relation to the position of the fulcrum (support). The arrows show the direction of movement of the load and effort.

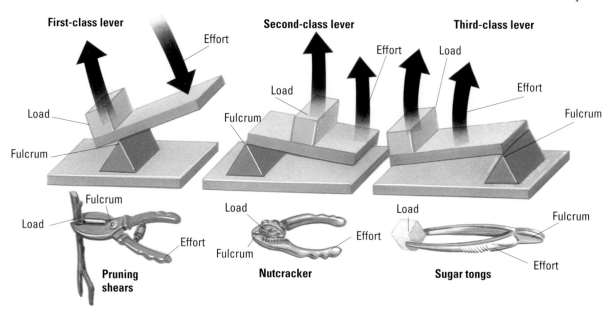

First-class lever — Load — Fulcrum — Effort — Fulcrum — Load — Effort — **Pruning shears**

Second-class lever — Load — Fulcrum — Effort — Load — Fulcrum — Effort — **Nutcracker**

Third-class lever — Effort — Load — Fulcrum — Load — Fulcrum — Effort — **Sugar tongs**

pair of sugar tongs. A third-class lever does not act as a force magnifier. The effort applied must be greater than the load. Its mechanical advantage is always less than one. However, a third-class lever magnifies movements. The load moves more than the effort. When you use sugar tongs, a small movement of the fingertips makes the jaws of the tongs move enough to grip a sugar cube. **PROJECT 50**

LEYDEN JAR (līd′n jär) A Leyden jar is a device for storing charges of electricity. It was invented in 1746 in the town of Leyden, Holland, by the Dutch scientist Muschenbroeck. It is the earliest form of capacitor, or condenser (see CAPACITOR AND CAPACITANCE). The electricity it stores is called static electricity (see ELECTRICITY).

A Leyden jar is a glass jar. Inside and outside it has a coating of metal for about half of its height. The mouth of the jar has a stopper of cork or wood. Through the center of the stopper is a movable brass rod. At the top of the rod is a brass knob. At the lower end of the rod is a brass chain. By raising and lowering the rod, contact can be made or broken between the chain and the inner metal lining of the jar.

To charge the jar, the brass knob is connected to an electrostatic machine. This produces an electrical charge by friction of glass, amber, or metal against silk, wool, or other material. The charge passes from the knob to the rod, the chain, and the lining of the jar. The outer metal covering of the jar is connected to earth. If the lining of the jar becomes negatively charged, the outside becomes positively charged. The positive and negative charges attract each other through the glass. They cannot pass through the glass, which does not conduct electricity. By raising the brass rod, contact with the lining is broken. The Leyden jar is now charged. Electricity can be stored like this for long periods. To discharge the jar, the outside is made to touch earth, and the chain is lowered. A highly charged jar gives a powerful electric spark.

LIBBY, WILLARD FRANK (1908–1980) Willard Libby was an American chemist. He was born in Grand Valley, Colorado, and was graduated from the University of California.

Libby was working with radioactive substances in 1945 when he heard about carbon 14. This is a radioactive isotope of carbon (see CARBON; RADIOACTIVITY). It has a very long half-life. More than five thousand years are needed for it to lose half of its radioactivity (see HALF-LIFE). Carbon 14 is always being made in the air. Plants take it in as a part of carbon dioxide and make it into plant tissues. Animals eat the plants and make them into animal tissues. When plants and animals die, they get no more carbon 14 in their tissues. All these facts made Libby think that carbon 14 could be used to find out how old certain things are.

He developed a way to date things from the amount of radioactive carbon 14 in them. Old things have less radioactivity than younger things. Libby's method has been used to decide on the age of many archeological finds. It is also useful in many other ways—for example, in discovering that a painting is a fake. Libby was awarded the Nobel Prize for chemistry in 1960 for his work on carbon 14.
See also DATING.

LICE Lice are tiny, wingless insects that live as parasites on birds and mammals (see PARASITE). Most lice are less than 0.2 in. [4 mm] long. They have flattened bodies, very short antennae, and strong claws on their feet for holding on to the hair or feathers of the host (the animal on which they live). Lice lay oval-shaped eggs called nits. Within a week, the nits hatch into nymphs (young lice),

LICE
Human head lice are difficult to get rid of. They can be killed by using a shampoo containing special chemicals.

which begin to move around immediately and attach themselves to the host. The life cycle of a louse—from egg to mature adult—takes about three weeks (see METAMORPHOSIS). Thus, a host is often never free from these pests. Most species of lice are host specific. This means that each species of louse attacks only one species of host.

There are two main groups of lice (order Phthiraptera). Chewing lice (or biting lice) belong to the suborder Mallophaga; sucking lice (or true lice) belong to the suborder Anoplura. Chewing lice usually attack birds, chewing feathers and biting the skin. Some species, however, attack mammals, including horses, cattle, and raccoons. Sucking lice live on warm-blooded animals, including human beings. They have sharp, beaklike mouths with which they make a hole in the skin and suck blood. They cause itching and irritation and sometimes spread such diseases as typhus (see TYPHUS). Lice spread very easily from one person to another, especially in crowded, unsanitary conditions. Many can be killed only with special chemical solutions sold as shampoos and medicines in drugstores. The tiny insects called plant lice are not related to the lice. *See also* INSECT.

LICHEN (lī′ kən) A lichen is an organism that is really two organisms, an alga and a fungus, living together symbiotically—that is, by helping each other (see ALGAE; FUNGUS; SYMBIOSIS). In a lichen the fungus absorbs water and minerals and passes them to the alga. The alga then uses them to make food by photosynthesis, and gives some of the food back to the fungus (see PHOTOSYNTHESIS). There are over eighteen thousand species of lichens, each of which has its own combination of alga and fungus species. Lichens grow all over the world in all kinds of climates. They can withstand extreme heat and extreme cold, and many of them grow in deserts and on high mountains.

Lichens have no leaves, roots, stems, or flowers. They are made of protective outer layers of fungal cells, inner fungal and algal cells, and stored food. Often, the algae are found mostly near the upper surface of the lichen, where they can get the sunlight that is necessary for photosynthesis to take place.

LICHEN
Lichens are combinations of algae and fungi that live together symbiotically—that is, they help each other survive. A crustose lichen is shown.

Most lichens have fungal strands that attach the lower surface to a tree or rock. These strands can also absorb minerals from the surroundings, and some can even dissolve the rocks to obtain minerals.

Most lichens grow very slowly, and some are more than four thousand years old. They reproduce in several ways. Soredia are tiny grains that form on the body of the lichen. These grains contain algal and fungal cells. They break off from the parent, and the wind or water carries them to another place, where they grow into new lichens. Isidia are much like soredia, except that they are peg shaped. Less often, lichens reproduce by spores (see SPORE). The spores are produced only by the fungi and must land near the right algae in order to form a new lichen. The lichen fungi cannot survive on their own, and for this reason lichens are sometimes regarded as a special group of fungi that can survive only with the help of the algae.

There are three main groups of lichens. Crustose lichens form a flat, crustlike covering on the substratum. The substratum is the surface to which the lichen attaches, such as soil, rock, or a tree trunk. Foliose lichens have flattened lobes, which look like tiny leaves on the substratum. They often grow on tree trunks and branches. Fruticose lichens look like tiny shrubs. They often form ground covers in arctic regions. One common species of fruticose lichen is reindeer moss, which is a major food source for caribou and reindeer in the Arctic.

Lichens have many uses. They are a food for animals and, in some countries, for human beings. Lichens provide a good ground cover and help prevent the erosion of soil in many areas (see EROSION). They are used in making medicines that act much like antibiotics (see ANTIBIOTIC). Lichens are also used in the manufacture of perfumes, soaps, and dyes. Lichens are the source of litmus, a chemical used to tell whether a solution is an acid or a base (see LITMUS). Lichens are very sensitive to sulfur dioxide, a poisonous gas that is part of air pollution. Because of this, scientists sometimes use lichens to monitor or measure the amount of sulfur dioxide present in the air in a given area.

LICORICE (lĭk′ ər ĭs)

Licorice is an herb of the pea family (see HERB; PEA FAMILY). Licorice flavoring, a very popular flavor, comes from the long, sweet roots and rhizomes of the plant, which are boiled to make a thick, brownish liquid. The solution is allowed to evaporate until only the extract (concentrated substance) remains (see RHIZOME).

Licorice in medicine hides the flavor of unpleasant-tasting drugs. Licorice is also used to flavor candy, soft drinks, chewing gum, and tobacco.

The licorice plant grows from 3 to 4 ft. [1 to 1.5m] high and has pale, pealike flowers. It grows in southern Europe and in parts of Asia. A small amount is grown in the United States. Over 40 million lb. [18 million kg] of dried licorice root is

LICORICE

The roots of licorice, which grows in the Mediterranean region and parts of Asia, provide a popular flavoring for candy.

brought into the United States each year. The root fibers remaining after the licorice flavor has been taken out are used to make a fire-fighting foam.

LIE DETECTOR

A lie detector is a machine that helps decide whether a person is telling the truth. A lie detector, also called a polygraph, records the way a person acts when asked questions. Changes in heartbeat, blood pressure, and breathing patterns may take place when a person lies. Also, a person may perspire more heavily when telling a lie.

The lie detecting unit is usually contained in a case that fits on a table. Wires lead from the unit to sensitive pickup instruments placed on parts of the person's body. A penlike object that makes lines on moving paper records changes in heartbeat.

Lie detectors are used by police and others trying to solve crimes. Because no machine can tell with absolute certainty whether a person is lying, the results of a lie detector test should be considered only in the light of other evidence. Many people question lie detector tests. They believe that testimony or information obtained this way may go against the Fifth Amendment to the Constitution of the United States. The Fifth Amendment says that one does not have to speak out against oneself. Many judges do not allow lie-detector testimony to be used in court.

No one can be forced to take a lie detector test. A person who agrees to do so answers a number of questions. Each question must be answered yes or no. If a person lies, the lie-detector chart may show a change in one or more of the body functions. If a person tells the truth, little or no change should take place. After a test, a lie detector expert "reads" the lines on the paper chart and interprets them.

In 1921, John A. Larson, an American psychologist, developed the first lie detector. In 1966, a group of Americans who worked with lie detectors formed the American Polygraph Association. This group watches over the use of lie detectors and decides what a person needs to know to qualify to use them. In 1972, the American inventor Allan Bell developed a lie detector called the psychological stress evaluator. The instrument finds slight tremblings in the voice that often occur when a person lies.

See also FORENSIC SCIENCE.

LIFE

Most people recognize things as either living or nonliving. For example, a dog is considered to be a living thing, but a stone is not. Scientists generally agree that to be alive, a thing must be able to grow and reproduce itself (see REPRODUCTION). It must also be able to use food to obtain energy for those activities (see FOOD). A living thing also responds to changes in its environment. It can adapt so that it or its offspring can survive (see ADAPTATION; ENVIRONMENT).

Biologists, the scientists who study life, have not yet discovered exactly how to divide living things from nonliving things (see BIOLOGY). For example, a virus alone cannot reproduce itself. However, it can enter the cells of living things and use parts of the living cells in order to multiply (see CELL). The question of what things are living, and the questions of how life began on Earth and whether life exists elsewhere in the universe, are among the great mysteries of science.

The origin of life

There are probably thousands of theories about how life began. Almost all religions teach that all forms of life were created by some divine or supernatural being or force. Another theory states that life originally came to Earth from outer space. According to this theory, dormant (inactive) stages of microorganisms carried in meteorites landed on Earth, where they grew and changed.

Most biologists and biochemists believe that life developed from nonliving material (see BIOCHEMISTRY). They believe that this development took place through a series of chemical reactions in the atmosphere. The atmosphere that existed on Earth at that earlier time was quite different from the atmosphere now. Experiments have shown that lightning and ultraviolet rays, passing through the kinds of gases that were probably in the earth's atmosphere at the time, could provide the energy needed to help form the component parts of proteins and nucleic acids from the elements in the gases. Life depends on the fact that the nucleic acids, which make up the chromosomes, can both duplicate themselves and supply instructions for the making of various proteins (see CHROMOSOME; NUCLEIC ACID; PROTEIN).

However, many other things were also necessary for the development of life as we know it. One major step was the formation of chlorophyll, through which the sun's energy could be trapped to form food by photosynthesis and to produce the oxygen needed by many forms of life (see PHOTOSYNTHESIS). Once organisms that could reproduce themselves had developed, the way was open for them to evolve into the vast range of living things that exist today (see EVOLUTION).

Some biologists work with astronomers to study whether life exists elsewhere in the universe (see EXOBIOLOGY; UNIVERSE). If certain physical and chemical conditions can allow life to evolve, then those conditions might be or might have been present on other planets as well as on Earth. Space travel since the 1960s has allowed study of the other planets in the solar system (see SOLAR SYSTEM; SPACE EXPLORATION). Scientists once thought life might exist on Venus or Mars. However, the information received from space probes showed this is not possible. Some scientists believe other intelligent life may exist far away in the universe. They are trying to communicate with this life by sending radio signals into space (see RADIO ASTRONOMY).

Characteristics of life

The basic activities of life are growth, reproduction, responsiveness, and movement. Living things take in food and other materials from their environment. Such substances take part in a complicated system of chemical changes known as metabolism (see METABOLISM). Waste products are excreted back into the environment (see EXCRETION). Metabolism creates the materials and energy for survival, growth, and movement. In organisms, growth often means more than an increase in size. An organism may grow by increasing the number of its cells (by cell division) or by increasing the size of its cells. Also, growth may be the development of new parts of

PRIMITIVE LIFE FORMS

Many-celled organisms first evolved in the sea. All of these strange-looking creatures lived on the sea bottom during the Cambrian period, about 550 million years ago. Their fossils have been found in the Canadian Rockies in layers of rock called Burgess shale.

the organism, or it may be regeneration, which is the replacement of a lost part (see GROWTH; REGENERATION).

In living things, many complex chemical molecules are arranged to form tiny organelles, which are parts of cells. Cells are the basic units of living systems. Some organisms consist of only a single cell (unicellular organisms), while others are made up of different types of cells (multicellular organisms). In multicellular organisms, cells are joined together to form tissues. Tissues make up the organs and other structures of the complete creature. At each of these levels of complexity, there is organization in activities, so that every molecule in the end contributes a little to the functioning of the whole system (see CELL; MOLECULE; ORGAN; TISSUE).

Most living things are capable of some kind of movement. People and many other animals stand, walk, and run. Fish swim. Birds fly. Some plants can even move under their own power (see MOVEMENT OF PLANTS). Nonliving things may also move. However, such movement—for example, a stone rolling down a hill—happens because of outside forces, such as gravity.

Another important property of living organisms is irritability. Irritability is the ability to respond to stimuli, such as heat or light. Green plants respond to light by growing toward it, for example.

Organisms can adapt to moderate changes in their environment. They can also repair damage to their own tissues and fight many diseases. Eventually, however, death occurs. This may occur due to different events, such as accident, disease, or natural aging (see DEATH). However, organisms reproduce themselves, so that their own kind survives (see REPRODUCTION). Reproduction may result in offspring with certain minor differences from their parents, such as a longer tail on a fish. Over many generations, these variations help species of organisms adapt to changes in their environment. The production of offspring with minor differences that may provide a survival advantage to future generations is the basis of the theory of evolution (see NATURAL SELECTION).

Chemical basis of life Living things are made up of the same chief chemical elements as nonliving things. The elements that occur in the earth, air, and water also occur in living organisms (see ELEMENT). Carbon, hydrogen, oxygen, nitrogen, sulfur, phosphorus, potassium, calcium, iron, and magnesium are the most common elements found in living things. Elements found in living things are mostly combined to form compounds. Organic compounds are found only in living things or their products. These compounds always contain both carbon and hydrogen. The organic compounds include carbohydrates, fats, proteins, and nucleic acids (see CARBOHYDRATE; FAT; PROTEIN). All these contain carbon, hydrogen, and oxygen. Proteins also contain nitrogen and often sulfur and other elements. Proteins exist not only in the form of enzymes, but also form the structural material of cells (see ENZYME). Fatty substances called phospholipids are also necessary to life. They form part of the membranes around and within cells. Some kinds of fats—and also carbohydrates—

supply or store energy for living things. A type of carbohydrate called cellulose forms the main structural material of plants. Another substance important for life is known as adenosine triphosphate (ATP), which is a chemical "messenger" important in the transfer of energy within living cells (see ATP). Vitamins are also very important. Many vitamins become coenzymes, which are substances that help enzymes carry out their tasks (see VITAMIN).

Since about 1950, discoveries made in molecular biology have given scientists an insight into how life processes are controlled. These discoveries have also added to the knowledge of how inherited characteristics are passed on from one generation to the next (see HEREDITY). The nucleic acids and proteins are now known to be the most important

KINDS OF LIFE

Biologists (scientists who study living things) recognize five basic forms of life, called the five kingdoms. The best-known kingdoms are plants, animals, and fungi. In addition there are the Monera (bacteria and blue-green algae), and the Protista, which include single-celled organisms and algae (except blue-green algae).

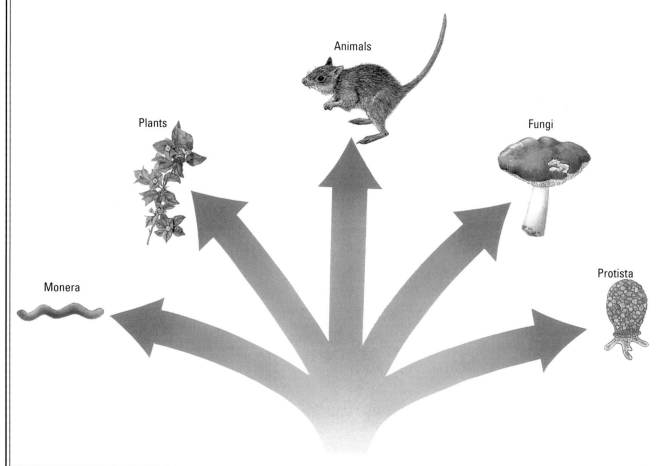

Animals

Plants

Fungi

Protista

Monera

EARLY LIFE

The lines visible in this rock formation are called stromatalites. They were produced by the action of blue-green algae, one of the first forms of life. Stromatalites are among the earliest fossils in existence.

substances of life. The nucleic acid DNA is the carrier of genetic information in cells. The chains of DNA—known as genes—are the coded instructions that form the basis of an organism's inherited characteristics (see CHROMOSOME; GENE; GENETICS). The coded message is translated into physical characteristics and metabolic processes by means of enzymes. The enzymes are manufactured according to the DNA's instructions with the help of another type of nucleic acid, known as RNA (see DNA; RNA).

Length of life When any organism approaches the end of its life span, certain changes have gradually taken place. The organism does not function as well as it did in youth. For example, an aging person's body takes longer to repair wounds. The tissues become less supple. Tough connective tissue replaces some muscular tissues. As a result, the muscles become weaker, and the walls of the arteries harden. Other physical changes may affect the brain and skin. Brain cells gradually deteriorate, and the skin loses its layer of fat and becomes wrinkled.

The potential length of life of all living things is basically determined by that organism's heredity. Many insects survive as adults for only a few hours, although they may have spent months or even years in the immature stages. The giant redwood trees of Oregon and California live for thousands of years.

Few humans live more than 100 years. Since 1900, the average length of life for an individual member of the population of the United States has increased by more than 25 years. A baby born in 1900 had a life expectancy of 47.3 years. By the early 1990s, a newborn boy could expect to live about 70 years, and a newborn girl, about 78 years. *See also* GEOLOGICAL TIME SCALE; MICROORGANISM; ORGANISM.

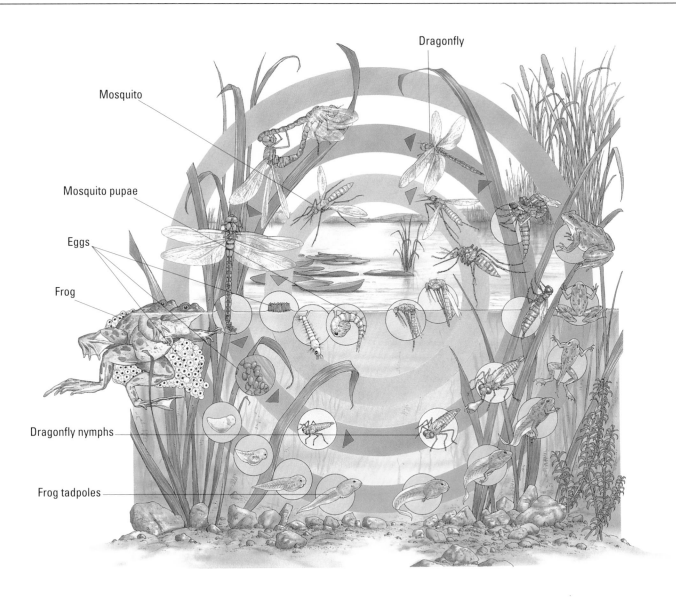

Dragonfly

Mosquito

Mosquito pupae

Eggs

Frog

Dragonfly nymphs

Frog tadpoles

LIFE CYCLE The life cycle of an animal or a plant is the sequence of events and stages that take place during its lifetime. In organisms that reproduce sexually, the life cycle begins with the fertilization of the egg and ends with the death of the individual. In human beings and most other vertebrates (animals with backbones), the life cycle is very simple. The young animal differs from the adult mainly in size, although it may also differ in color, and it gradually grows into an adult. The life cycle of a frog is rather more complicated (see FROG). Each individual frog exists in two quite different forms—the tadpole and the adult—during its life. But the tadpole still grows gradually into the adult form. The life cycles of butterflies and bees are even more complex (see BEE; BUTTERFLY AND MOTH). After hatching from the egg, the insect

LIFE CYCLE—Aquatic young

Frogs, mosquitoes, and dragonflies all lay their eggs in water. The young—tadpoles, pupae, and nymphs—also remain underwater until they develop into adults. The adults leave the water, but must return to breed and complete the life cycle.

passes through three different stages: larva or caterpillar, pupa or chrysalis, and adult (see CHRYSALIS). In each case the individual changes from one form to another during its life cycle and reproduces only in the adult stage (see INSECT; METAMORPHOSIS).

There are even more complex life cycles, especially among the jellyfish and the parasitic flatworms (see JELLYFISH). These creatures exist in two or more completely separate forms and reproduction takes place in at least two of them. The life cycle for these creatures can start at any point, and it includes all the different stages passed through until the original stage is reached again. Fern life

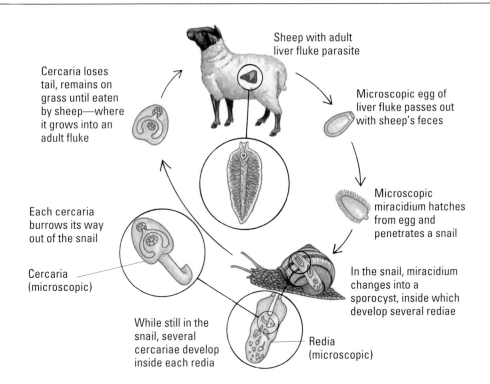

Cercaria loses tail, remains on grass until eaten by sheep—where it grows into an adult fluke

Sheep with adult liver fluke parasite

Microscopic egg of liver fluke passes out with sheep's feces

Microscopic miracidium hatches from egg and penetrates a snail

Each cercaria burrows its way out of the snail

Cercaria (microscopic)

In the snail, miracidium changes into a sporocyst, inside which develop several rediae

While still in the snail, several cercariae develop inside each redia

Redia (microscopic)

LIFE CYCLE—Parasite and host

The life cycle of a sheep liver fluke is one of the most complicated known. Flukes, which are flatworms, are parasites in both vertebrate and invertebrate animals. The sheep liver fluke passes from one host, a sheep, to another, a snail, and then back again to a sheep. It changes form six times: egg, miracidium, sporocyst, redia, cercaria, and adult liver fluke.

cycles also involve two quite separate stages—the fern plant itself and a tiny green disc called a prothallus (see FERN). The fern scatters spores that grow into prothalli, and then the prothalli produce sex cells that pair up to produce new fern plants (see ALTERNATION OF GENERATIONS).
See also LIFE.

LIGAMENT A ligament is a band of tough fibrous tissue that holds organs of the body, such as the heart, in place and fastens bones together. A ligament is a kind of connective tissue that is strong as rope (see CONNECTIVE TISSUE). When ligaments covering a joint are twisted or torn, a sprain occurs. A sprained ankle is a partial tearing of the talofibular ligaments that bind the bones of the lower leg to the bones of the foot. Torn or twisted ligaments heal slowly. If they are completely torn apart, they may never heal. When a sprain occurs, doctors use plaster casts, tape, or elastic bandages to bind the injured limb and limit movement. This takes the pressure off the injured joint and allows the ligaments to heal.

Athletes who get minor sprains often put ice packs on the injury for the first day and then later bathe the injured limb in a whirlpool bath. A whirlpool bath is a tub of hot, swirling water. The heat of the water and its fast-flowing action against the injured area help the ligaments heal more quickly by improving blood circulation.
See also SPRAIN.

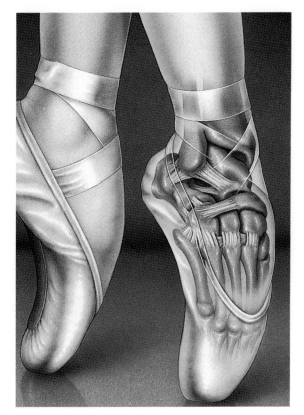

LIGAMENT
Ligaments are bands of tough fibrous tissue that fasten bones together. For example, ligaments bind the bones of the foot (above).

LIGHT

Light is a form of energy. It is radiant energy, or radiation. This means that it spreads out from any source in which it is produced.

We talk of light as traveling in waves. However, these are not like waves on the ocean or sound waves (see WAVE). Waves at sea need water to exist. Sound waves are vibrations of molecules in the air or in another substance. In contrast, light waves can travel even in a vacuum. In fact, they travel faster in a vacuum than anywhere else (see VACUUM). Light waves are changes in electric and magnetic fields. They are a form of electromagnetic radiation (see ELECTROMAGNETIC RADIATION).

The complete range of waves that we can see is called the visible spectrum. It is a tiny part of the range of waves that make up the electromagnetic spectrum. Just outside the visible spectrum are infrared rays and ultraviolet rays. We feel infrared rays as heat. We can also notice the effect of ultraviolet rays. They are the rays in sunlight that can give the skin a tan or burn (see SPECTRUM).

There are also gamma rays, X rays, microwaves, and radio waves, as well as others. We can see none of these, though they may be traveling constantly around us or even through us. Our eyes are sensitive only to light waves (see RADIATION).

How light behaves We say that we can see rays of light streaming through a window. However, it is not the rays of light from the sun that we see. It is sunlight that has been reflected from small dust or smoke particles toward our eyes. We can only "see" a ray of light if it shines straight into our eyes. Light that goes past us without striking anything is quite invisible.

We see a glowing object because its light reaches us directly. We see other objects because they reflect light back to us. Different colors, surfaces, and shapes reflect light differently. The different reflections form images in our eyes. The brain then determines what the various reflections mean. It tells us whether we are looking at a tree, a chessboard, or a printed page (see EYE AND VISION).

When light strikes something with an uneven surface, it bounces off in many different directions. The rays become scattered. However, when light hits a perfectly flat surface, the rays bounce off together, all in the same direction. Rays striking a mirror are reflected and travel onward in a straight line again. They are reflected from the surface at exactly the same angle as the angle at which they struck the mirror. This is one of the laws of reflection (see REFLECTION OF LIGHT).

Sunlight

Metal grid

Electrons flow out

Silicon layers

Electrons flow in

Metal backing plate

SOLAR CELL

A solar cell (above) converts sunlight into electricity. It consists of two layers of silicon sandwiched between a metal grid and a metal backing plate. Electrons flowing between the silicon layers and then in the metal form the electric current.

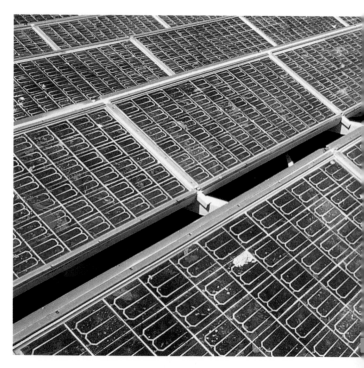

No surface reflects all the light that strikes it. A certain amount of the light is always absorbed, or taken up, by the surface itself. The energy of the light is taken up by the molecules it strikes. It is converted into heat or another form of energy, such as chemical energy or electrical energy. The darker the color of the surface, the more light is absorbed and lost. This is why black mirrors, no matter how flat and polished, are not as good as bright silver mirrors. Black mirrors absorb more light than they reflect.

Rays of light can be refracted, or bent, by transparent substances. This happens when light passes from air into water or from air into glass. The rays turn and travel at a slightly different angle, in another straight line. We make use of this to design lenses of glass and plastic. Lenses are used in eye glasses, microscopes, telescopes, and other optical instruments. We can bend the rays of light as we want. The light can be brought to a single point, or focus (see LENS). On the other hand, when light passes through a prism, the different wavelengths are bent at different angles, and the light rays separate from each other. They form a spectrum of all the colors that make up white light (see COLOR; DISPERSION OF LIGHT; PRISM; REFRACTION OF LIGHT).

In nature, raindrops act like tiny prisms. Sunlight reflected and refracted inside raindrops produces the colors we see in rainbows. Refraction is also responsible for the way a stick appears to bend when it is put into water. It is why fish in water are never where they seem to be.

What is light? For thousands of years, people tried to understand the true nature of light. The ancient Greeks thought that light was rays of matter given out by whatever object was being looked at. The Greek philosopher Plato and his followers believed that it was a mixture of matter coming from the sun.

In the seventeenth century, the British scientist Sir Isaac Newton put forward two theories (see NEWTON, SIR ISAAC). One was that light is matter (see MATTER). The other was that light is wave energy. The puzzling thing about the wave theory was that light does not seem to behave like sound waves or water waves. Newton rejected the wave theory because he thought that light could not bend like these other waves. However, another scientist, Christian Huygens of Holland, did believe in light waves. He said that light was vibrations that are at right angles to the direction of travel. The waves spread at great speed and in straight lines. He said that they moved in the ether. Ether was believed to be an invisible substance that was spread everywhere.

Scientists obtained clues when they examined shadows of objects. Shadows do not have perfectly sharp edges. This is hard to explain unless light acts as a wave. A wave passing the edge of a solid object spreads out as it does so. This effect is called diffraction (see DIFFRACTION).

Another property of waves is interference. When two waves arrive at a point, they interfere with one another. If the high parts and low parts of the waves arrive in step, their effects are added, or reinforced. However, when the high part of one wave arrives at the same time as the low part of the other, the waves cancel each other out. This can be shown to happen with light. Light shining through two pinholes onto a screen produces a pattern of light and dark rings on the screen. This can be explained as light

RANKS OF CELLS

There are 1,500 solar panels in this array at the Kirkpatrick Center in Oklahoma City (below). Together they produce 120 kilowatts of electricity.

waves from the pinholes interfering. Where the waves are in step, a bright ring is produced. Where they cancel out, a dark ring is formed. The patterns formed are called interference fringes. Again, light is behaving like waves (see INTERFERENCE).

Observations such as this led scientists to put forward the electromagnetic theory of light. The Scottish physicist James Clerk Maxwell was mainly responsible for this theory (see MAXWELL, JAMES CLERK). He discovered many laws that show how electric and magnetic effects work. He calculated how fast these effects would take place. He showed that the speed agreed very closely with the velocity (speed in a certain direction) of light. Radio waves, discovered by Heinrich Hertz, were also found to travel at this speed. Scientists realized that all these waves belonged to the same family of radiations, the electromagnetic spectrum.

Light behaves like vibrations at right angles to the direction of travel. The vibrations are up and down, side to side, and at every angle in between. By cutting out vibrations in every plane but one, we can polarize light. Polarized light vibrates in only one plane. This is done by using a polarizing filter (see POLARIZED LIGHT).

However, in some ways, light does behave like particles rather than waves. For example, when light strikes a metal surface, it may knock electrons out of the metal's atoms. The moving electrons form an electric current. It is as though the electrons had been knocked by other particles of a definite size. This is called the photoelectric effect (see PHOTOELECTRIC EFFECT). To explain this, scientists say that light can be regarded as streams of photons. These are little packets of light energy that behave as though they were particles. All electromagnetic radiation is given out like this, in units called quanta. The quanta behave both like particles and waves of energy. Long-wavelength radiation seems to behave more like waves, as in radio waves. Short-wavelength radiation, such as X rays, behaves in many ways more like particles (see PHOTON; QUANTA).

Light and color The light we see is made up of different wavelengths. The short wavelengths form the blue end of the spectrum. The long wavelengths form the red end. Between are the other colors. When we see a mixture of all the colors together, we see white light.

Different substances absorb different wavelengths of light. They reflect others. When we see a red object, it means that all the wave lengths but red have been absorbed by the object, and only red is being reflected back to our eyes. White paper reflects almost all the wavelengths of light that strike it. In the same way, black paper absorbs almost all the wavelengths of light.

Colors can be selected with color filters. A red glass filter allows only light of the red wavelength to pass through. It absorbs all others. Seen through a red filter, a green object appears black because no green light can pass through the filter. A filter can be made that will absorb all light wavelengths equally. This is called a neutral density filter. Often, such filters are used in sunglasses. They do not change the colors of things seen through them.

Speed of light All electromagnetic radiation travels at the same speed in a vacuum. The speed has been measured to be approximately 186,282 mi. [299,792 km] per second. It is thought that nothing can travel faster than this. The light from distant stars reaches us only many years after it has set out on its journey. PROJECT 41, 43, 44, 52, 68

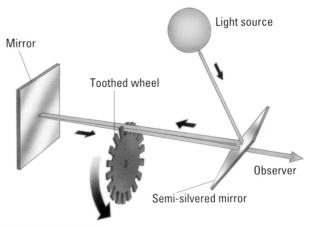

SPEED OF LIGHT

The French physicist Hippolyte Fizeau measured the speed of light by bouncing a beam of light between two mirrors placed 5.5 mi. [9 km] apart. A rotating toothed wheel interrupted the beam until the wheel was speeded up. When the beam became continuous, Fizeau knew that the light had gone from the wheel to the mirror and back in the time it took for the wheel to rotate by only one tooth. Knowing the distance and the time, he could calculate the speed of light.

LIGHTHOUSE A lighthouse is a building, usually a tower, that holds a light for guiding sailors in darkness or fog. Lighthouses have been used for thousands of years. The ancient Romans built lighthouses throughout their empire. The Pharos lighthouse of Alexandria, a wonder of the ancient world, had a tower 394 ft. [120 m] tall, with a fire at the top. Lighthouses today have lights bright enough to be seen many miles away. Often they have foghorns too.

Lighthouses are usually stone or cast-iron towers that are wider at the base than at the top. They are built on rocks or small islands near harbors and ports. Lighthouses must be very strong to withstand powerful storms and seas. Some are fully automatic in operation and need no one to tend them.

The light is the most important part of the lighthouse. It often has a huge barrel-shaped lens, known as a Fresnel or classical lens, about 8 ft. [2.4 m] high and 6 ft. [1.8 m] in diameter that encircles the lamp. This type of lamp sends out a flashing light that may be seen as far as 19 mi. [32 km] out to sea.

LIGHTHOUSE

The light from a lighthouse guides sailors at night or in bad weather. Pictured here is the Cape Hatteras lighthouse in North Carolina.

Lighthouses also have radio beacons. Radio beacons give out radio signals that are an aid to sailors in fog.

Each lighthouse has its own color or shape. At night, each one sends out its own pattern of colored lights or flashes. Sailors at sea can tell which lighthouse they see by looking in a book called *Light Lists.*

LIGHTNING Lightning is a static electric charge that moves from a cloud to the ground, from the ground to a cloud, or from one cloud or part of a cloud to another (see CHARGE; ELECTRICITY). Lightning usually goes with thunderstorms, though it sometimes is seen during snowstorms, dust storms, and volcanic eruptions.

Lightning is caused by an electric current flowing between two charged bodies. In a thunderstorm, huge cumulonimbus clouds (thunderheads) become highly charged (see CLOUD; CURRENT, ELECTRIC). If the thunderhead comes close enough to a body of opposite electric charge, such as the earth's surface, a visible spark, or lightning, results. Lightning may also occur between parts of the same cloud or between two different clouds. One bolt of lightning may measure more than fifteen million volts (see VOLT).

When lightning travels through the atmosphere, it heats up the air around it. The heated air expands, compressing (squeezing) the colder air nearby. This causes air waves that result in thunder.

Types of lightning There are several kinds of lightning. Chain lightning zigzags from a cloud to the ground. It often forks into many branches before reaching the earth. Most injuries are caused by chain lightning.

Sheet lightning is a bright flash that lights up the sky. It is really light from chain lightning beyond the horizon. Heat lightning is faint sheet lightning that is so far away that no thunder can be heard.

Ball lightning is made up of balls of fire that drop from clouds. It usually explodes when it hits the ground. Most scientists believe that ball lightning is an optical illusion—that is, people only think they see it. However, it has been produced in a laboratory (see OPTICAL ILLUSION).

Lightning can be very dangerous. In the United States, lightning kills one person and injures another four every day. People use lightning rods to protect buildings from lightning. A lightning rod takes the electricity from a bolt of lightning to the earth, thus preventing injury or damage. The safest place to be during a lightning storm is in a car or in a building that has lightning rods. Dangerous places include under a tree, on a hilltop, or in a body of water.

See also THUNDERSTORM.

LIGHTNING
Lightning is a high-voltage electrical spark that usually flashes from a thundercloud to the ground.

LIGHT-YEAR A light-year is the distance that light travels in one year. Light moves at a speed of about 186,282 mi. [299,792 km] per second. One light-year is equal to 186,282 miles times the number of seconds in a year, or 5.88 trillion mi. [9.46 trillion km]. The light-year is used to measure the great distances between the earth and the stars. The closest star to the earth (apart from the sun) is about four light-years away.

LIGNIN (lĭg′ nĭn) Lignin is a very tough substance found between the walls of cells in woody plant tissue. It is brownish in color and it gives timber much of its strength. Together, cellulose and lignin make up most of the fibers of wood.

See also CELLULOSE.

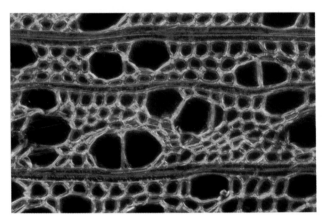

LIGNIN
Lignin "glues" together the fibrous tissue of wood, shown here in magnified cross section.

LIGNITE (lĭg′ nīt′) Lignite is a low-quality brown or black coal. It is between peat and bituminous coal in the coal-formation process (see COAL).

Lignite is not widely used as fuel. Raw lignite contains 20 to 60 percent water. When dried, brown lignite's carbon content is between 60 and 75 percent. Black lignite may be more than 80 percent carbon. Lignite is mined in North Dakota and Texas in the United States and in Australia, New Zealand, Germany, India, and Japan.

LIGNITE
Lignite is dug out of huge open-cast mines. This mine in Australia yields 4 million tons of lignite each year.

LILAC The lilac is any of thirty species of flowering plants belonging to the genus *Syringa* of the olive family, Oleaceae (see OLIVE FAMILY). Lilacs are shrubs or small trees that grow in cooler areas of the world. Lilacs have simple leaves that are dark green and heart shaped. Bunches of purple, blue, or white flowers grow at the ends of the stems.

The common lilac grows 20 ft. [6 m] tall. It has wide, spreading branches and large bunches of sweet-smelling flowers. Most cultivated lilacs are varieties of this species, which originated in southeast Europe.

LILAC

Lilacs are valued for their colorful, fragrant flowers that bloom in late spring.

LILY FAMILY The lily family includes more than two hundred genera (plural of *genus*) with about four thousand species of plants. These monocotyledons (one seed-leaf plants) grow all over the world (see MONOCOTYLEDON). The leaves generally have parallel venation (veining) (see LEAF). Bunches of six-segmented (six-part) flowers grow on long stalks. Most members of the lily family grow from bulbs, corms, or tubers, which store food (see BULB AND CORM; TUBER).

The genus *Allium* is generally considered part of the lily family. This genus includes several plants that can be eaten, including garlic, leek, onion, and shallot. The genus *Lilium* includes about eighty species of plants known as true lilies. The flowers are funnel shaped and may be any of several colors (see FLOWER). The Easter lily, with its pure white flowers, and the tiger lily, with its purple-spotted golden flowers, are two popular species of lily. Other members of the lily family include aloe, asparagus, hyacinth, lily of the valley, and tulip. Several species yield valuable medicinal drugs.

The most serious disease of members of the lily family is called mosaic. Mosaic is caused by a virus carried by aphids.

LILY FAMILY

Lilies have characteristic six-petaled flowers, often with darker spots or stripes. Shown here are varieties known as tiger lily (top) and leopard lily (bottom).

LIMESTONE Limestone is a kind of rock made chiefly of calcium carbonate (see CALCIUM CARBONATE). It is usually gray, white, or tan.

Much limestone forms from the shells and skeletons of dead sea animals. These are rich in calcium carbonate. They collect on the ocean floor and finally are changed into limestone.

Some limestone is formed by inorganic means (that is, means that do not involve living things). Under certain circumstances, water containing calcium carbonate evaporates, leaving behind the calcium carbonate, which eventually hardens into limestone.

Chalk is a soft, white, porous (containing holes) limestone made up of shells of microscopic organisms. The best-known chalk deposits are of the Cretaceous period, which ended about 65 million years ago. These include the famous White Cliffs of Dover in England (see CHALK).

If weak acid is poured on limestone, it gives off bubbles of carbon dioxide. This is a common way of telling if rock is limestone.

Limestone is widely used for buildings and highways. It is very easily carved. Most limestone used for building in the United States is taken from the earth in Indiana. If limestone is exposed to extreme heat and pressure, it becomes the metamorphic rock known as marble (see MARBLE).

Limestone dissolves in rainwater containing carbon dioxide, forming topography with outcrops of limestone. Groundwater also dissolves limestone, sometimes forming caves.
See also CAVE.

LIMPET Limpets are marine or freshwater gastropods with bowl-shaped or conical shells that cover the entire body (see GASTROPOD). Most limpets are less than 3 in. [7.5 cm] long, though one species reaches a length of 8 in. [20 cm]. Limpets have a strong, muscular foot that grips the rocks very firmly.

The common American limpet lives on rocks along ocean coasts. When covered by high tide, the limpet glides along on its foot, feeding on algae. It moves food into its mouth with its radula, a thin, tonguelike part with several rows of teeth. It does not move very far, however, and returns to its resting place before low tide. The limpet attaches itself to a rock by making a strong suction with its foot. The shell is pulled down so tightly over the animal that seabirds and other predators (animals that eat other animals) find it very hard to get it off.

LIMESTONE

The limestone "pavement" (top) is a natural feature formed when a slab of limestone is crisscrossed by deep cracks. The jagged limestone peaks (below) were formed by erosion.

LIMPET

Limpets can be found on rocks at low tide. When the tide comes in (high tide), the limpets move around to feed.

LINDEN The linden is a tree that belongs to the genus *Tilia*. It is often called a basswood. Lindens have large, plain leaves. The trees grow to 120 ft. [37 m] tall. Two of the 30 species are native to North America. The small-leaved European linden has also been planted in North America. Lindens are also known as limes in Europe, but must not be confused with the citrus trees of that name.

LINDEN

European lindens are often planted in a row to protect crops from the wind.

LINNAEUS, CAROLUS (1707–1778) (lĭ nē′ əs, kăr′ ə ləs) Carolus Linnaeus was a naturalist born in Sweden. He is famous for inventing today's international system of naming living organisms (see CLASSIFICATION OF LIVING ORGANISMS).

Linnaeus grew up in the south of Sweden, in beautiful countryside full of wild flowers. For a short time, he studied medicine. However, he was more interested in botany (the study of plants). His love of plants led to his becoming a professor of botany.

Other scientists had tried various ways to classify plants. Linnaeus began a system of classification based on the reproductive organs of plants. In time, he moved to Leyden, Holland, and started work on a grand scheme to classify both plants and animals. This was first published in 1735 and called the *Systema Naturae* (System of Nature).

Linnaeus invented the binomial (two-name) system of naming species. He put together species that seemed to be much alike and gave them the same name. This was the generic name (a name for all members), and the group was called a genus. Then he gave each species in a given genus a second name. All these second names were different. For example, the lion, the leopard, and the tiger are scientifically known as *Panthera leo*, *Panthera pardus*, and *Panthera tigris*, respectively. Because they all share the generic name *Panthera*, we know immediately that they are closely related.

Linnaeus did not believe in evolution. Most of his system of classification has now been dropped. However, we still use his simple system of names.

LION The lion is a large, powerful member of the cat family. The lion's thundering roar, great strength, and majestic appearance all account for its being called the "king of beasts." Lions once lived in Europe, the Middle East, India, and much of Africa. As a result of killing by humans, there are no more lions in Europe, the Middle East, or northern Africa. Most lions live in Africa south of the Sahara desert. About two hundred lions still live in the Gir Forest of India.

Male lions are the only cats with long manes. This collar of thick hair covers the head (except the face) and neck down to the shoulders and chest. Most males are about 9 ft. [2.74 m] in length, including the tail. They usually weigh from 350 to 400 lb. [160 to 180 kg]. The female lions, called lionesses, are somewhat smaller, weighing from 250 to 300 lb. [115 to 140 kg].

The color of the lion's coat makes it easy for the animal to hide. It is a brownish yellow, like the color of dead grass. Young lions, called cubs, have spots on their coats. By the time the cubs are a few months old, the spots disappear.

The lion is the most sociable of all cats. Males are sometimes seen alone, but usually the animals live in groups called prides. A pride may include anywhere from six to thirty-five animals, though from

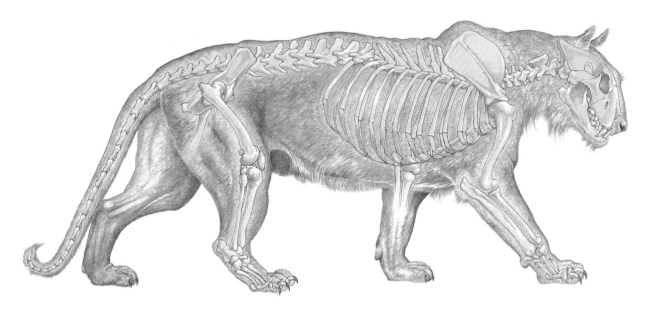

LION

A lion's body is ideal for an efficient predator (above). A lion has sturdy bones, powerful muscles, and sharp teeth and claws. By day, male lions rest or keep watch (left), while the females go hunting.

ten to twenty is more common. Each pride has from one to three adult males, several lionesses, and some cubs. Each pride stays in a certain area called a territory (see TERRITORY). The territory holds the food and water that lions need. Where prey is plentiful, territories may be about 15 sq. mi. [39 sq. km]. If prey is scarce, the territory may cover 100 sq. mi. [260 sq. km].

Lions do not allow strange animals to hunt in their territory. They warn them to stay away by roaring or by squirting a mixture of scent and urine on bushes. The strangers then know that the territory belongs to others. If they ignore the warnings, they may be killed. The adult males defend the pride and fight strangers. However, the lionesses do most of the hunting. Sometimes, several lions hunt together. While some hide, others circle the prey and chase it toward the waiting lions that are hidden in the high grass. Lions feed mainly on zebras and antelopes. The adult males eat first. The lionesses and cubs have to wait until the adult males are finished.

LIQUEFACTION (lĭk′ wə făk′ shən) Liquefaction is the changing of gases into liquids. Gases often can be changed into liquids by compressing (squeezing) them. However, many gases can be liquefied only if they are also cooled. Every gas has a critical temperature. Above this temperature it will not turn into liquid, no matter how much pressure is applied (see GAS).

Some gases can be liquefied at room temperature. Ammonia and carbon dioxide are examples. Ammonia has a critical temperature of 270°F [132°C], while for carbon dioxide the critical temperature is 90°F [32°C]. Liquid ammonia and liquid carbon dioxide can therefore be prepared by compression alone. Liquid carbon dioxide is interesting because it can only exist under pressure. When it is exposed to the air, it starts to evaporate. This causes so much cooling that the liquid freezes into solid carbon dioxide, or "dry ice." The solid then changes directly into carbon dioxide gas.

Nitrogen's critical temperature is -233°F [-147°C]. A temperature as low as this cannot be reached in ordinary refrigerators, so liquid nitrogen is somewhat difficult to prepare. A special method of cooling was invented in Germany in the mid-nineteenth century. In this method, nitrogen gas is circulated from a vessel around loops of pipes. In one part of the system, a pump is used to compress the gas. The compressed gas is allowed through a small nozzle. As the gas expands again, its temperature drops. The cold gas is then pumped through a coil in the vessel that holds the still-warm gas. This cools the warm gas. Finally, all the gas in the system becomes so cold that the critical temperature is reached. Drops of liquid nitrogen are formed.

The gases hydrogen and helium are even harder to liquefy. The critical temperature for hydrogen is -400°F [-240°C] and for helium is -450°F [-268°C]. To be cooled, these gases are put into containers cooled by the evaporation of other liquid gases. In the case of hydrogen, liquid air is used. As the liquid air evaporates, it takes up the necessary heat from the hydrogen. The temperature of the hydrogen falls below the critical point. It can then be liquefied. To liquefy helium, cooling is first produced by the evaporation of liquid hydrogen. *See also* EVAPORATION.

LIQUID Liquid is one of the three states of matter. Gas and solid are the other two (see STATES OF MATTER). In some ways, a liquid is like a gas. A liquid's molecules are not fixed to each other in any special way. Also, a liquid takes the shape of its container. In other ways, a liquid is unlike a gas and like a solid. A liquid has a certain volume (see VOLUME). Also, the molecules of a liquid are only slightly compressible (able to be pressed into less space).

Surface tension is a force that occurs at the surface of a liquid. It is caused by the attraction of molecules for each other. Surface tension acts something like a skin (see SURFACE TENSION).

The molecules of a liquid often have a greater attraction for other substances than they have for each other. Because of this, the molecules of a liquid will rise in narrow tubes above their own level.

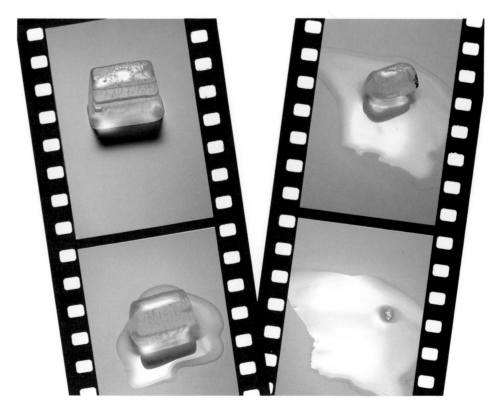

LIQUID—Melting
Ice is a solid, and like nearly all solids, it gradually melts to form a liquid (water) when heated.

LIQUID—Condensation
A liquid is formed when a gas or vapor is cooled sufficiently. Here, mist—a collection of small water droplets—forms as water condenses out of the damp evening air as the temperature drops.

This is called capillary action. Plants draw water in this way (see CAPILLARY ACTION).

If liquids are heated beyond a certain point, they turn into gas. Water changes to steam. If cooled beyond a certain point, liquids change into solids. Water freezes to ice. Different liquids have different boiling and freezing points.

Substances that are gases can be cooled and compressed into a liquid state. Also, some substances that are solid can be heated until they turn into a liquid. *See also* LIQUEFACTION; LIQUID AIR. **PROJECT 7, 19**

LIQUID AIR Liquid air is air that has been cooled until all the gases that make it up have turned into liquid (see GAS; LIQUEFACTION; LIQUID). Liquid air is a mixture of liquid oxygen, liquid nitrogen, and liquid argon. It has a pale bluish color.

Air can be liquefied by cooling it to -328°F [-200°C] at normal atmospheric pressure. Under high pressure, it can be liquefied at temperatures up to -222°F [-141°C], but no higher. This is the critical temperature of air.

Liquid air is made by compressing (squeezing) air to a very high pressure. The compressed air is then allowed to expand rapidly. This cools the air to a very low temperature.

Liquid air is a refrigerant—that is, it is used to produce low temperatures in other substances. It must be handled very carefully. Its temperature is so low that it turns rubber and flesh into hard, brittle solids and mercury into solid metal. It must be kept in special vacuum flasks.

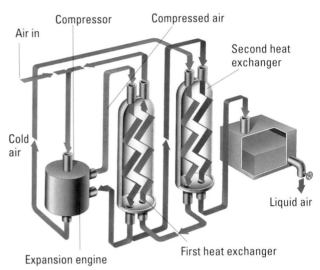

LIQUID AIR
Air enters the compressor, where it becomes heated. The warm compressed air is then cooled in the first heat exchanger. Part of this air passes to an expansion engine, where it expands and drives the compressor. As the air expands, its temperature falls. In the second heat exchanger, the rest of the air is cooled by the cold expanded air. However, since this air is compressed, it has a higher boiling point than the expanded air and eventually liquefies.

LISTER, JOSEPH (1827–1912) Joseph Lister was a British surgeon. He was working at the Glasgow Royal Infirmary (hospital) in Scotland when he began the research that made him famous.

At that time, nearly half the patients in hospitals were dying after operations because their cuts became infected. Lister set out to try to find out why this happened. While he was experimenting, he read about Louis Pasteur's work on disease-causing microorganisms in France (see PASTEUR, LOUIS). He decided that microorganisms were the cause of infection. He found a chemical called carbolic acid to be antiseptic, which means it killed microorganisms on living tissue (see ANTISEPTIC).

Lister made the use of carbolic acid (now called phenol) a rule in his hospital. Hands, surgical cuts, and wounds all had to be washed with this antiseptic. Ignaz Semmelweis had already stressed the importance of hand washing as a means of preventing infection after childbirth in Vienna, Austria. However, Semmelweis's work was not widely known and was rejected by the medical profession. Lister was a well-known surgeon who had already made important discoveries. Because of this, and Pasteur's work, Lister was able to convince other doctors about the value of antiseptics. He was made a peer (a lord) in 1897.

LITHIUM (lĭth′ ē əm) Lithium is a metallic element. It is the lightest of all the metals and belongs to the family of alkali metals. It has the chemical symbol Li (see ALKALI METAL; ELEMENT).

Lithium is a very reactive element. It reacts with water to form hydrogen gas. It burns readily in the air with a bright white flame. In cases where the temperature is not too high, the flame color is crimson and is used to identify the metal.

Lithium is mixed with other metals to form alloys (see ALLOY). It can be alloyed with lead and aluminum to harden them and with beryllium to soften it. Compounds of lithium and other elements are used in making pottery and glass. They are also used in storage batteries and as coloring agents in signal flares. One compound, lithium carbonate, is a very effective drug used to treat manic depression, a type of mental illness.

In nature, lithium is found in the ores lepidolite, spodumene, and amblygonite. It is also found in some mineral springs. The pure metal is produced by the electrolysis of lithium hydride (LiH). Lithium aluminum hydride ($LiAlH_4$) is a powerful reducing agent (see ELECTROLYSIS; OXIDATION AND REDUCTION).

Lithium was discovered by the Swedish chemist Johan Arfvedson in 1817. Its name came from *lithos,* the Greek word for "stone." Lithium's atomic number is 3, and its relative atomic mass is 6.941. It melts at 356°F [180°C] and boils at 2,456°F [1,347°C]. It has a valence of one in its compounds (see VALENCE).

LITHOSPHERE AND ASTHENOSPHERE

(lĭth′ ə sfĭr′; ăs thĕn′ə sfĭr) The two parts of the earth's structure involved in plate tectonics are the lithosphere and the asthenosphere (see PLATE TECTONICS). The lithosphere is the rigid outer shell of the earth. It is divided into brittle plates that cause earthquakes as they slide past one another. The asthenosphere is the softer, hotter layer beneath the lithosphere. It moves somewhat like seawater beneath a layer of ice, but as a plastic (nonrigid) substance rather than as a liquid. The lithosphere consists of the crust and the topmost rigid part of the mantle (see CRUST; MANTLE). It is about 62 mi. [100 km] thick and forms the plates themselves. The asthenosphere is a solid but plastic layer near the top of the mantle. Occasionally

LITHIUM

The red color in this Fourth of July fireworks display at Fort Laramie, Wyoming, comes from lithium compounds.

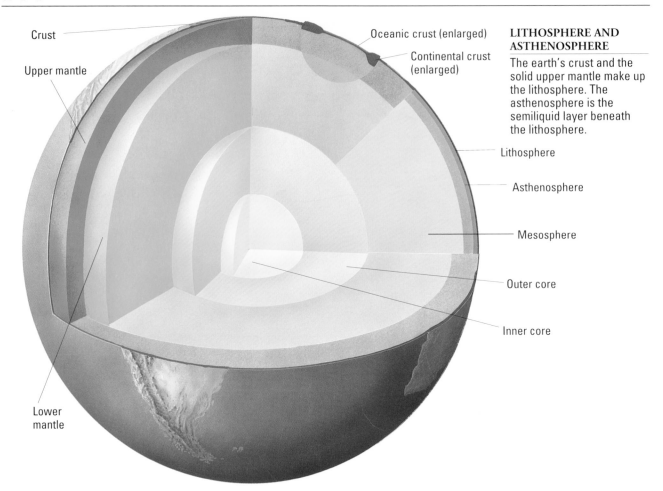

Crust

Upper mantle

Lower mantle

Oceanic crust (enlarged)

Continental crust (enlarged)

LITHOSPHERE AND ASTHENOSPHERE
The earth's crust and the solid upper mantle make up the lithosphere. The asthenosphere is the semiliquid layer beneath the lithosphere.

Lithosphere

Asthenosphere

Mesosphere

Outer core

Inner core

parts of it melt and feed magma chambers leading to volcanoes. Scientists know that the asthenosphere exists, because they have observed that earthquake waves go much more slowly through this region than they would if it were as rigid as the lithosphere. During the formation of mountains or during ice ages, the greater weight on the surface pushes the lithosphere down into the asthenosphere. The asthenosphere floats away plastically to make room for the lithosphere. When a glacier melts or a mountain range is eroded away, the lithosphere rebounds and the asthenosphere flows back into the space formed.

LITMUS Litmus is used in chemistry to discover the presence of acids and bases. Litmus is a dye made from organisms called lichens. It is either red or blue in color and is used in the form of a solution, which is sometimes on test paper (see LICHEN).

Bases turn red litmus blue or deep violet. Acids turn blue litmus red. Neutral solutions (neither base nor acid) do not change the color of litmus. A common laboratory experiment is to dip pieces of litmus paper into chemical solutions to see if they are bases, acids, or neutral.

When a chemist wishes to neutralize an acid solution, he or she adds litmus first. This turns the solution red. The base is then added until the solution changes to a violet color. The solution is then exactly neutral. One more drop of base turns it blue. *See also* ACID; BASE; NEUTRALIZATION.

LITMUS
The left-hand flask contains an acid that has turned litmus red. The base in the right-hand flask has turned litmus purple.

The liver is a large and important organ located in the abdomen of all vertebrates (animals with backbones). Among invertebrates, only mollusks have an organ resembling the liver. The liver can be thought of as a living laboratory and chemical factory. It carries out many functions, all concerned with regulating the chemistry of the body. More than a hundred different processes are known to take place in the liver.

Among other things, the liver is concerned with the digestion of food, excretion of wastes, storage and conversion of food materials, addition of important components of the blood, and the destruction of poisonous substances. The liver is a vital organ. If it stops working completely, death occurs within a few hours (see DIGESTION; EXCRETION).

In an adult human, the liver weighs about 3 lb. [1.5 kg]. It is found on the right-hand side of the body. The liver is tucked under the ribs and is protected by them. It is reddish brown in color and has an irregular triangular shape, with a rounded upper surface. The liver is divided into four lobes, or sections, by the structures running through it. Pressed tightly under it is the gallbladder. The ancient Greek name for the liver was *hepar*. The adjective for all things related to the liver, *hepatic,* comes from this.

The liver has a rich blood supply. The blood that supplies oxygen to the liver cells comes from the aorta, which is the main artery leaving the heart. The blood reaches the liver through a branch called the hepatic artery. The liver also receives blood from the intestines. This blood carries food materials that have been absorbed through the intestinal wall. It reaches the liver through the hepatic portal vein. After it has been processed and filtered, blood leaves the liver through the hepatic vein to return to the heart. The main food materials that the liver deals with are glucose and amino acids. The amino acids come from the digestion of proteins. The sugar glucose is stored in the liver as glycogen (a starchlike carbohydrate). It can be released, as necessary, to provide fuel for the body's cells (see GLUCOSE).

Amino acids are used by the liver to build proteins for the blood plasma (see BLOOD). Some amino acids are used to make more glucose. One of the waste products of this process is urea. Urea is removed from the body by the kidneys. Amino acids cannot be stored in the liver like glucose. They must be used immediately (see AMINO ACID; PROTEIN; UREA).

The liver aids digestion by producing bile. Bile is a liquid that is stored in the gallbladder before being poured into the duodenum of the small intestine. Bile salts aid in the digestion of fats (see BILE; GALLBLADDER). The liver also acts as a storage place for vitamins, iron, and copper.

A very important function of the liver is the destruction of harmful chemicals present in the blood. Alcohol, other drugs, and many poisons are destroyed or changed into harmless substances in the liver. This process is known as detoxification. The detoxified chemicals are then passed from the body in the urine.

See also CIRRHOSIS; HEPATITIS.

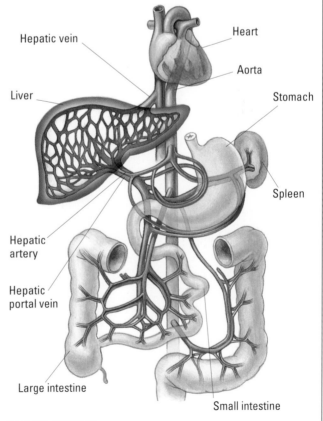

BLOOD SUPPLY

The liver receives blood from the heart, via the hepatic artery, and from the digestive system, via the hepatic portal vein.

LIZARD

The Chinese xenosaur (top) is an unusual lizard that lives in streams. The sungazer (middle) uses the spines on its tail for defense. A lizard wriggles from side to side as it walks (bottom). This action resembles the swimming movements of amphibians, from which lizards evolved.

Chinese xenosaur

Sungazer

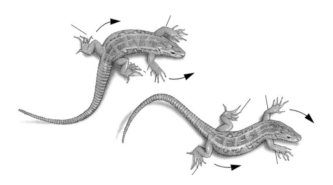

LLAMA (lä′ mə) The llama is a humpless mammal belonging to the camel family, Camelidae. It may have descended from the guanaco (see GUANACO; MAMMAL). The llama is a domestic animal

LLAMA

Llamas were first tamed hundreds of years ago by the Incas who lived in the Andes Mountains of South America. They used the llama to carry heavy loads through the mountains. Today, the llama is raised mainly for its wool.

LIZARD A lizard is a type of reptile. It is closely related to the snakes. Some lizards are hard to tell apart from snakes because they do not have legs. However, most lizards do have legs, as well as eyelids. No snakes have eyelids (see REPTILE; SNAKE).

Like the snakes and other reptiles, lizards are vertebrate, cold-blooded animals with scaly skins (see COLD-BLOODED ANIMAL; VERTEBRATE). Most lizards lay eggs, but some species give birth to live young. Lizards vary in size from just a few inches long to over 10 ft. [3.05 m].

There are about three thousand species of lizards, which live all over the world. Most live in tropical regions. Very few lizards live in cold lands. Lizards can run fast and climb; some can even "swim" through sand or glide through the air. Two species are poisonous. Lizards eat many different things. Most feed on insects.

that was probably first tamed five hundred to six hundred years ago by the Incas living in the Andes Mountains of South America. They used the llama as a pack animal because it is surefooted in the mountains and able to carry heavy loads for long periods of time with no water and little food. Llamas are grazing herbivores (plant-eating animals) and eat lichens, shrubs, and other plants which grow in the mountains.

A llama stands about 4 ft. [1.2 m] tall at the shoulder and is about 5 ft. [1.5 m] long. It has a dense coat of long, coarse hair that is usually white but may be brown or black. Female llamas usually start to mate before they are two years old. After a gestation period of eleven months, the female gives birth to one kid (baby llama). She nurses the kid for about three months and protects it for another two.

The only defense a llama has against an enemy is kicking or, more often, spitting a foul-smelling juice in the attacker's face. A llama may also do this if tired or overburdened. At these times, a llama may also lie down and refuse to move. Llamas are valued for their meat, wool, and solid wastes, which can be dried and used for fuel.
See also CAMEL.

LOAD In a machine, the load is the object to which the effort is applied, using the machine's mechanical advantage (see MACHINE, SIMPLE). A pulley, for example, magnifies the effort so that it can be used to lift a heavy weight—the load. With a pulley, the effort is applied by pulling one end of the rope around the pulley. The force to lift the load is produced at the other end of the rope. In a machine, the effort is usually smaller than the load. The ratio of load to effort is the mechanical advantage of the machine.

LOAM Loam is a rich, fertile kind of soil. Sand, silt, and clay are almost equally mixed in loam. This gives loam the best characteristics of each kind of particle. Unlike sand, loam holds moisture well. Unlike clay, loam has enough gaps in it to allow air to reach down into it. The silt often provides nutrients (food). In order for plants to grow well, moisture, air, and nutrients must all be in a soil. Sandy loam is loam with more sand than silt and clay. Loams with more silt or clay are called silty loam or clayey loam, respectively.
See also SOIL.

LOBELIA (lō bēʹl ē ə) *Lobelia* is a genus of about 200 species of flowering plants in the family Lobeliaceae. They grow mainly in tropical and subtropical regions and include trees and shrubs as well as many annual and perennial herbaceous plants (see ANNUAL PLANT; HERBACEOUS PLANT; PERENNIAL PLANT). There are clusters of two-lipped, tube-shaped, but somewhat irregular flowers. These clusters grow in racemes on the plant stem (see INFLORESCENCE).

Lobelias are popular garden flowers. Blue lobelia has bright blue flowers and is often planted on the edges of gardens and in hanging baskets. It is sometimes called edging lobelia or trailing lobelia. The cardinal flower is popular because of its bright red blossoms.

LOBELIA
The cardinal flower, a type of lobelia, grew originally in the rain forests of Central America.

LOBSTER The lobster is a sea crustacean that lives on the bottom of the ocean, usually close to shore. Its hard exoskeleton covers the lobster's body. Lobsters are prized as food and are usually caught in pots baited with dead fish. The exoskeletons of most kinds of lobster are dark green or dark blue and spotted. When lobsters are cooked, their exoskeletons turn bright red (see CRUSTACEAN; SKELETON).

The common lobster of North America, called the American lobster, is 12 to 24 in. [30 to 61 cm] in length. It weighs 1 to 20 lb. [0.5 to 9 kg]. Most European lobsters are smaller than American lobsters.

A lobster has five pairs of jointed legs. Four pairs are thin, and the lobster uses them for walking. The front pair are usually large and have huge claws. One of the claws is very heavy, having thick teeth to crush prey. The other claw is smaller. It has sharp teeth to tear food apart. The big, heavy claw is not on the same side on all lobsters. Some lobsters are "right-handed." Others are "left-handed." Not all lobsters have large front claws. Lobsters eat crabs, snails, small fish, and other lobsters. Lobsters also eat dead organisms.

LOBSTER

The lobster classified as *Scyllarides latus* (top) has ten short legs. It lives among rocks and lacks the massive claws of the European lobster (bottom).

A female lobster usually lays eggs once every two years. She may lay 5,000 to 100,000 or more eggs at one time. She carries them around for nearly a year until they are ready to hatch. Older females lay more eggs than young ones do.

Lobsters molt (cast off their exoskeletons) as they grow. Two days after being hatched, the lobster loses its first exoskeleton. It molts three more times during the first month. Each time the lobster molts, it produces a new, very soft exoskeleton (see MOLTING). The animal hides from its enemies until the new exoskeleton hardens. A lobster may live as long as fifteen years.

LOCK A lock is a device that prevents the opening of a door, window, or gate, or the use of a machine. Many locks operate with keys. The key is placed in the lock. The grooves of the key force metal pins or tumblers to align. When the tumblers are in line, the key can turn. The turning action moves a sliding bolt, or lever, that locks or unlocks. Instead of a key, some locks have a cylinder and a number of small wheels. The cylinder is turned to certain stops shown by numbers on a dial until all the wheels are lined up in a certain way. Then the lock can be opened. This kind of lock is called a combination lock. The average combination lock has from 100,000 to 1 million possible combinations. Time locks are used on heavy bank vault doors. They are large combination locks that also have a clock. Such locks are set to open at a certain time each day.

There are two main kinds of key locks. They are lever-tumbler locks and pin-tumbler cylinder locks. The lever-tumbler is a catch inside the lock. The catch slides into a slot in the bolt and prevents it from moving. Some kinds of lever-tumbler locks have two lever tumblers held to the bolt by springs. When the right key is placed in the lock, the lever tumblers are lifted to the right height to clear the slots in the bolt as the key turns. As the key turns, it reaches another slot in the bolt, and moves it from one side to the other.

The pin-tumbler cylinder lock is common today. The main part of this lock is called the plug. It is found inside a cylinder. There are pairs of pins of different lengths with springs that find holes in the plug and cylinder. The upper pin of each pair prevents the plug from being turned. A flat key is placed in a slot in the plug. Ridges on the edge of the key lift the pins so that the upper ones just clear the plug. The key can then be turned, causing the plug to turn and the lock to work.

Key locks are used on doors, windows, automobile starter switches and steering wheels, and so on. Computers often have a lock that must be opened with the right key before they can be turned on.

Padlocks are locks that are mostly used outdoors. A padlock has a *U*-shaped bolt attached to a small case. One end of the bolt is always attached to the casing, but the bolt is able to turn. When the lock is opened by turning the key in a slot in the case, or by dialing the correct combination, one end of the bolt can be pulled free. The bolt can then be

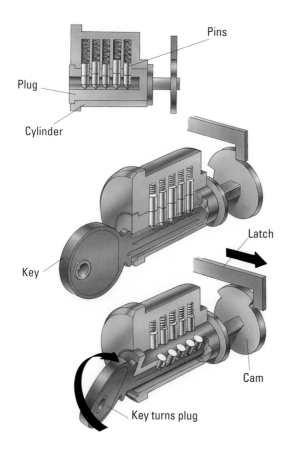

LOCK

A pin-tumbler cylinder lock is shown in sideways section at the top, without the key in position. Spring-loaded pins prevent the plug from turning. When the key is inserted (center), it lifts the pins to different heights so that they clear the plug. The plug will then turn in the cylinder (bottom) so that a cam will move the latch.

slipped through loops of metal on the item to be locked. The free end of the bolt is then lined up with the hole in the case it came from. It is pushed down into the hole, where it catches and locks. One kind of padlock is the bicycle lock. It has an extra-long *U*-shaped bolt that can be slipped between the spokes of a wheel and around a part of the frame. This prevents anyone from stealing the bike by riding it away.

Magnetic solenoid locks are often used on outside and inside doors and gates of business places and private clubs. Such a lock works by electricity when a person pushes a button somewhere away from the door. This gives the person pushing the button a chance to see who wants to enter. Keycards, invented in the early 1980s, have a magnetically imprinted code that allows the lock to open. The code can be easily changed when the lock is to be used by another person.

The first locks with keys were used in Egypt over four thousand years ago. Both the locks and the keys were made of wood. The metal lever-tumbler lock was invented in 1778 by Robert Barron, an English locksmith. The pin-tumbler cylinder lock, or yale lock, was invented in 1865 by Linus Yale, Jr., an American locksmith. Another American, Henry Robinson Towne, joined with Yale to produce Yale's new lock.

LOCK (NAVIGATIONAL) A navigational lock is a stone or concrete chamber built where two parts of a canal or river are at different levels. The lock has large, watertight gates at both ends. Locks come in many sizes. Most are from 400 to 1,200 ft. [120 to 366 m] long and 66 to 110 ft. [20 to 34 m] wide.

Locks make it possible for boats and ships to move from one water level to another. For example, Lake Erie is about 325 ft. [100 m] higher than Lake Ontario. However, a group of locks in the Welland Canal allows ships to pass from one lake to the other. The Welland Canal connects the two lakes.

After a ship or boat enters a lock, the gates close behind it. If the ship or boat is going from a lower level to a higher level, water is pumped into the lock through channels called sluices. When the

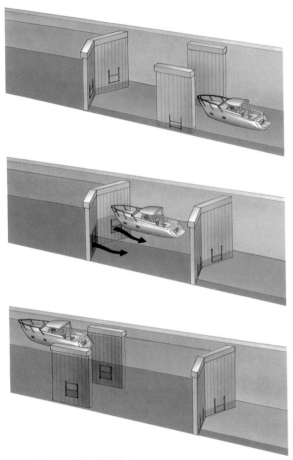

LOCK (NAVIGATIONAL)
To go to a higher level, a boat enters the lock (top). The gates are then closed behind it, and water is allowed in through channels called sluices (center). When the water levels are the same inside and outside the upper gates, the gates are opened and the boat continues on its way (above).

LOCOMOTION
A human walks by pushing the foot against the ground at an angle, so that it presses down and back (below).

water level in the lock is the same as the level in the next part of the waterway, the other gate opens, and the ship or boat goes on its way. When one is moving to a lower water level, water is pumped out of the lock instead.

The gates and sluices in most locks work by electricity. In the Panama Canal locks, ships do not use their own engines to move through the locks. Small railway engines on either side of the locks tow the ships with long cables.

See also CANAL.

LOCOMOTION Locomotion is the ability of an organism to move itself from place to place. Most biologists consider locomotion to be one of the characteristics that separate animals and animallike organisms, such as protozoans, from plants and plantlike organisms, such as algae (see ALGAE; ANIMAL KINGDOM; PLANT KINGDOM; PROTOZOA). Locomotion helps animals and animallike organisms find food, shelter, and mates. It also helps them flee predators. Locomotion is brought about in very different ways. For example, a kind of protozoan called an ameba moves by projecting a part of its body, called a pseudopodium, forward. The rest of the ameba's body then oozes up to the pseudopodium. In contrast, humans move by means of a complex system of bones, joints, muscles, and tendons.

See also AMEBA; MUSCLE; SKELETON.

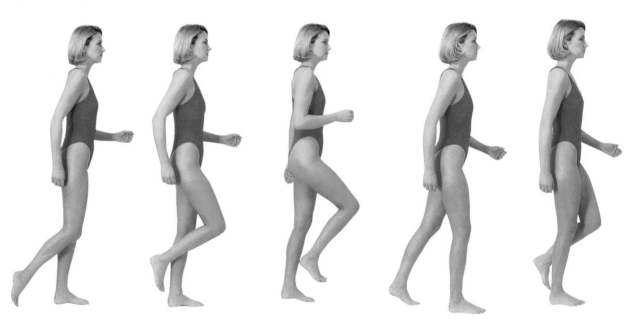

LOCOMOTIVE

A locomotive is a vehicle that moves train cars on railroad tracks. Modern locomotives weigh over 700 tons [640 metric tons] and can move more than two hundred loaded freight cars at once. The three main kinds of locomotives each depend on different power sources—steam, a refined form of petroleum called diesel oil, and electricity. The rest of this article will deal with these kinds of locomotives. A fourth kind of locomotive is powered by a gas turbine (see ELECTRICITY; ENGINE; GAS TURBINE; PETROLEUM; STEAM ENGINE).

Steam locomotives Steam locomotives contain steam engines. Locomotive steam engines usually produce heat by burning coal or oil. The heat turns water in the locomotive's boiler into steam. The steam is fed into cylinders. There, the pressure from the steam drives pistons up and down. The pistons are connected to the wheels by rods. The rods pass on the movement of the pistons to the wheels. Steam locomotives have an attached car, called a tender, that carries fuel and water. Steam locomotives are not very efficient. They must burn

THE ROCKET
The *Rocket*, built by George Stephenson in 1829, is pictured (left). It was the first successful commercial steam locomotive. It reached a speed of about 30 m.p.h. [48 kph].

PUFFING BILLY
The steam locomotive at right, built by William Hedley in 1813, was used to pull carts at coal mines in order to save horse labor. Because it was very noisy, it was named *Puffing Billy*.

AMERICAN DESIGN
A typical steam locomotive of the mid-1800s is shown at left. The large lamp mounted in the front was used to light the track at night. The slanted device in front of the wheels pushed aside obstacles that appeared on the track. It was called a cowcatcher.

huge amounts of fuel to produce power. They require much maintenance and cannot maintain the high speeds of diesel or electric locomotives.

The first steam locomotive was built in 1804 in England by Richard Trevithik. In 1825, Colonel John Stevens built the first steam locomotive in the United States. However, both of these locomotives had various problems. In 1829, George Stephenson, another Englishman, developed the first successful steam locomotive. The steam locomotive was important in the westward expansion of the United States in the mid- to late 1800s. People could reach new areas to settle and establish trade.

Steam locomotives once powered most railroad trains. In many countries, steam locomotives continue to power most railroad trains. However, in the United States, diesel locomotives have almost

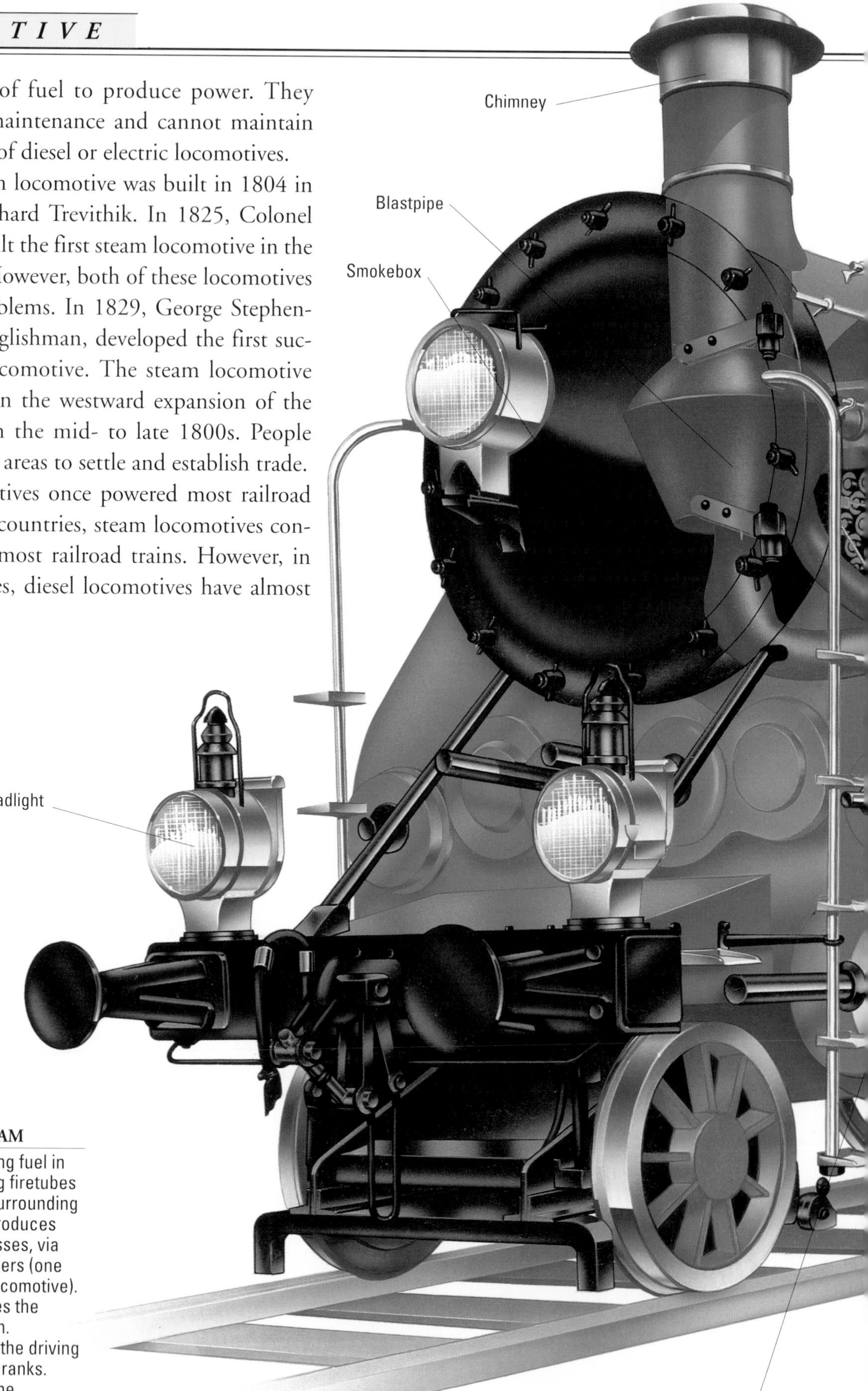

Chimney

Blastpipe

Smokebox

Headlight

PRINCIPLE OF STEAM

Hot gases from burning fuel in the firebox pass along firetubes in the boiler. Water surrounding the tubes boils and produces steam. The steam passes, via valves, into the cylinders (one on each side of the locomotive). Steam pressure moves the pistons back and forth. Connecting rods turn the driving wheels by means of cranks. Exhaust steam from the cylinders passes up the chimney. This creates a draft that pulls the hot gases through the firetubes. Smoke also goes up the blastpipe.

Cylinder with piston

completely replaced steam locomotives. Today, most steam locomotives in the United States are used to power tourist trains.

Diesel locomotives Diesel locomotives are powered by diesel engines (see DIESEL). Diesel locomotives have several advantages over the steam locomotives they have largely replaced. They can travel farther without needing refueling. They

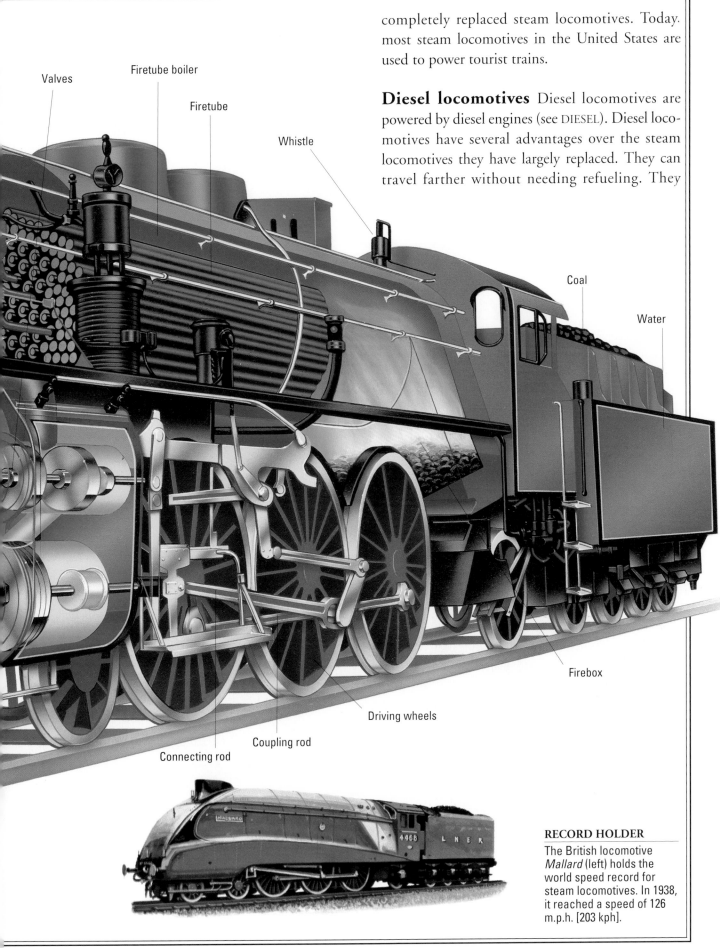

Valves

Firetube boiler

Firetube

Whistle

Coal

Water

Firebox

Driving wheels

Coupling rod

Connecting rod

RECORD HOLDER
The British locomotive *Mallard* (left) holds the world speed record for steam locomotives. In 1938, it reached a speed of 126 m.p.h. [203 kph].

LARGEST LOCOMOTIVE

The largest steam locomotive, called *Big Boy*, was built to pull heavy freight trains over the Rocky Mountains. It had two sets of driving wheels, each with their own cylinders. A mechanical stoker fed coal to the firebox at the rate of 9 tons per hour.

start, speed up, and stop faster than steam locomotives. They also cost less to maintain. Up to six diesel locomotives can be connected in one train for more power.

The most common kind of diesel locomotive in the United States is actually a combination of a diesel locomotive and an electric locomotive. In the diesel-electric locomotive, the diesel engine drives a machine called a generator. The generator creates an electric current (see GENERATOR, ELECTRICAL). The

current is fed to motors called traction motors. The traction motors drive gears that turn the wheels.

Another kind of diesel locomotive, called a diesel-hydraulic, is common in Europe. In hydraulic machines, power is provided by the force and motion of liquids. In a diesel-hydraulic locomotive, a diesel engine powers a pump. The pump forces oil against the blades of a turbine. The turbine in turn drives gears that turn the wheels (see TURBINE).

Small locomotives may have a diesel-mechanical design. A diesel-mechanical locomotive works much the way an automobile does (see AUTOMOBILE). The diesel engine sends power through a system called a mechanical drive train. The drive train has clutches, gears, and shafts, which all work to turn the wheels.

Electric locomotives Many people were involved in the development of the electric locomotive. In 1879 the German company Seimens and Halske built the first practical electric

ELECTRIC AND DIESEL

The *Mistral Express* (right, top) was put into operation in France after World War II (1939–1945). One of these electric locomotives achieved a world speed record of 205 m.p.h. [328 kph] on a special test run. In a diesel-electric locomotive (right, bottom), the diesel engine powers a generator, which provides electric power to work the traction motors. These motors drive gears that turn the wheels.

locomotive. Thomas Edison, the great American inventor, tested his first electric locomotive in 1880 (see EDISON, THOMAS ALVA).

Electric locomotives do not produce their own power. They obtain power from an electric-power plant that may be miles away. Wires or rails deliver the power from the plant to the locomotive. Most electric locomotives in the United States use alternating current (see ALTERNATING CURRENT). The alternating current travels in an overhead wire called a catenary. A steel framework called a pantograph connects the overhead wire with the locomotive. The electric current is then fed into traction motors. The traction motors usually drive gears that turn wheels.

Electric locomotives that use direct current receive this current from a rail that runs between the tracks (see DIRECT CURRENT). A metal device called a contact shoe is attached to the locomotive and slides along the rail. The contact shoe picks up the electricity and delivers it to the locomotive.

Like diesel locomotives, several electric locomotives can be connected for more power. Electric locomotives are more powerful than diesel locomotives. They are especially useful for high-speed passenger and freight trains. Electric locomotives are also quieter than other locomotives and release no exhaust. Thus, they are often used in and around large cities and for underground railroads called subways.

See also MAGNETIC LEVITATION VEHICLE; RAILROAD.

HIGH-SPEED TRAIN

Modern high-speed trains have a locomotive at either end. These locomotives may be powered by gas turbine engines or electric motors, as here with the train that runs through the Eurotunnel between England and France.

LOCOWEED Locoweed is the name for several species of plants in the pea family (see PEA FAMILY). Locoweed is a native of western North America. The plants are members of two genera (plural of *genus*), *Astragalus* and *Oxytropis*. A few of the species in each genus cause a disease in animals called locoism. This condition particularly affects cattle, which may eat the locoweed while grazing. Locoism affects the nervous system. Its characteristic symptoms are hallucinations, a slowness in walking, and lusterless hair. The disease can end in death.

Gum tragacanth, a substance used in the textile and paper industries, comes from several species of *Astragalus,* but none of those causes locoism. Some other species accumulate selenium, a rare element that is important to industry, from the soil. The occurrence of those species may indicate the presence of selenium in soil. Selenium poisoning from these locoweeds is responsible for the death of large numbers of cattle. Selenium poisoning is also called locoism but is not related to the other disease of that name. Nonpoisonous species of *Oxytropis* called point vetch are sometimes used for sheep fodder.

LOCOWEED
Locoweeds are members of the pea family. This nonpoisonous species, in the genus *Astragalus*, was photographed in Arizona.

LOCUST Locusts are several species of large grasshoppers with short antennae. They belong to the family Acrididae (see ANTENNAE; GRASSHOPPER). These insects are up to about 2 in. [5 cm] long and have large heads and eyes. Locusts are usually scattered over a fairly large area, tending to live

LOCUST
Migratory locusts have darker colors than locusts in their solitary phase. Migratory locusts form huge swarms that can destroy whole crops.

alone. Such locusts are said to be in the solitary phase. Sometimes, however, weather and food conditions cause the number of locusts to increase in a certain area. The females lay their eggs in the soil in cases containing about twenty to one hundred eggs each. When these eggs hatch, the nymphs find themselves even more crowded. This overcrowded condition may trigger the migratory phase (also called gregarious phase).

In the migratory phase, the locusts tend to be darker in color than their usual pale brown or green. They have stronger, larger wings, and they tend to stay together. These migratory locusts are much more active, have higher body temperatures, and lay many more eggs than solitary locusts. As a result, their numbers increase dramatically. The locusts form swarms of billions of individuals and begin to migrate. During the migration, the swarm may be so large and dense that it blocks out the light from the sun. Swarms sometimes travel great distances without causing much damage to plants. When the swarm settles in a new area, however, the damage can be devastating.

Swarms of locusts may descend on crops or other plants like a huge blanket. A swarm once covered 2,000 sq. mi. [5,200 sq. km] near the Red Sea in the Middle East. When a swarm lands, the locusts eat all the plants in the area, often leaving nothing but bare ground. If the swarm continues to migrate, it leaves a path of destruction behind. The swarm may continue growing for several generations until its size is controlled by the weather or by humans' using insecticides or other artificial means to destroy the eggs before they hatch. Attempts to control the swarm itself have rarely been successful, because it is usually spread over a very large area.

Locusts have swarmed in almost all the warmer parts of the world. In the 1870s, a swarm of Rocky Mountain locusts caused millions of dollars' worth of damage to crops in the Mississippi River valley in an area extending from Canada to Texas. Swarms sometimes move over large bodies of water. A swarm was once sighted more than 1,180 mi. [1,900 km] from land. Swarms occur most often in Africa and Asia. One of the most frequently swarming locusts in these areas is the desert locust.

When a swarm begins to die out, the remaining locusts revert to the solitary phase. Experiments have shown that it is the environment (in particular, the density of the locust population) that determines whether a locust is gregarious or solitary. Gregarious locusts raised in isolation become solitary in appearance and behavior. Solitary locusts raised in crowded conditions become gregarious or migratory in appearance and behavior.
See also INSECT; MIGRATION.

LOCUST (TREE)

Locust is the name of about twenty species of trees and shrubs of the genus *Robinia*. It is a member of the pea family (see PEA FAMILY). These trees and shrubs are native to North America, mainly in the eastern part of the United States. Some species do occur in the southwestern United States and in Mexico.

Locusts produce flowers in long, branched clusters. They also have long, papery pods that contain hard seeds. Along the branches, where the compound leaves are attached, are pairs of sharp spines.

The black locust, a tree that grows to about 98 ft. [30 m] in height, is native to the mountain areas of the eastern half of the United States, but it is now planted widely in other areas. The tree produces fragrant white flowers in the spring. Its wood is very heavy and was once used in shipbuilding. Now locust wood is used mainly for craft items and posts.

LOCUST (TREE)
The honey locust, also called carob, has nutritious seedpods that contain more than 50 percent sugar.

The clammy locust is a shrub or small tree about 33 ft. [10 m] high. It is native to the mountains from Pennsylvania to Alabama. The honey locust is actually a member of a different genus of the pea family.

LODESTONE

Lodestone, also spelled loadstone, is a naturally magnetized variety of the mineral magnetite (see MAGNETISM; MAGNETITE). The

LODESTONE
Lodestone, a naturally magnetized form of the mineral magnetite, attracts steel objects such as this paper clip.

magnetic properties of lodestone were known in ancient times. In about A.D. 1200, it was discovered that an oblong piece of this stone, if hung by a string, would point to the north and south. People called this stone a "leading stone."

Lodestone made possible the invention of the compass. This helped sailors navigate more accurately, because they no longer had to steer only by the stars (see COMPASS).

Lodestone is found in Russia, on the island of Elba in the Mediterranean Sea, and in the United States (especially Magnet Cove, Arkansas).

LOESS (lō′ əs) Loess is a type of fertile soil usually deposited by the wind. It is a yellowish material containing clay, sand, organic material, and a variety of fine-grained minerals. Loess is found in the central and northwestern United States, central and eastern Europe, and eastern China.

Most of the loess in the United States is the result of glaciation. The retreating glaciers of the ice ages left muddy plains behind them. Eventually, the plains dried, and the wind blew the topsoil farther south. This settled on the ground as loess. In China, loess came from the deserts in the eastern part of the country.

See also EROSION; GLACIATION; SOIL.

LOGARITHM (lŏ′ gə rĭth′ əm) Logarithms enable us to work out difficult multiplication and division problems quickly and accurately. By using logarithms, multiplying two numbers is replaced by adding two numbers, and dividing is replaced by subtracting.

Every positive integer (whole number) has a logarithm. The logarithm can be found by using tables of numbers called logarithm tables. Sometimes, these are called log tables. There are also antilogarithm, or antilog, tables. Antilog tables enable one to find a number knowing only its logarithm. Today, calculators and computers can find logarithms without the need for tables.

The number 32 is equal to five 2s multiplied together: 2 x 2 x 2 x 2 x 2. This is often written as 2^5. The number 5 is called the index or the power. 2^5 is read as "two to the power of five." In the same

way, 8 equals 2 x 2 x 2, or 2^3. Suppose that we want to multiply 32 by 8. All we have to do is to add the two indices (plural of *index*) together:

$$32 \times 8 = 2^5 \times 2^3 = 2^{5+3} = 2^8$$

2^8 equals 256; therefore, 32 x 8 = 256. A multiplication has been turned into an addition. If we want to divide one number into another, then the indices are subtracted:

$$32 \div 8 = 2^5 \div 2^3 = 2^{5-3} = 2^2 = 4$$

A division has been turned into a subtraction. $2^8 = 256$ is an equation. This equation can be written in a different way. It can be written as $\log_2 256 = 8$. The small "2" is called the base of the logarithm.

We can think of a logarithm as an exponent. Notice that $\log_2 256 = 8$ is saying that the power or index of 2 that is required to yield 256 is 8. Alternatively, $2^8 = 256$. This inverse relationship between logarithmic equations and exponential equations is a valuable tool for mathematicians and scientists. For example, the age of ancient items can be determined by using exponential and logarithmic equations.

Any number can be used as a base for a logarithm. Very often the base 10 is used. It is the easiest base to use for working out problems. These logarithms are called common logarithms. Scientists and mathematicians often use a system of logarithms in which the "number" *e*, equal to about 2.718, is the base. These are called natural or Napierian logarithms. Logarithms were invented by a Scottish mathematician, John Napier, in the 1600s.

LOGIC GATE A logic gate is a kind of switch that will operate only if certain conditions apply. One kind of logic gate will only let an electric current pass—that is, will have an output—if a current is present in each of two inputs. This type of logic gate is called an AND gate. Another type will give an output if either of two inputs is on. This is an OR gate. A third type will give an output if its single input is off, or if its input is on; this is a NOT gate.

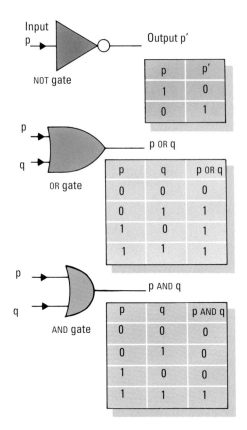

LOGIC GATE

Three important kinds of logic gates are the NOT, OR, and AND gates. A NOT gate has only one input; the others have two. The tables show outputs for every possible combination of inputs.

Combinations of logic gates are used widely in security equipment. They trigger alarms if doors or windows are open, for example. They are also used widely in computers, where several million logic gates can be placed on a single semiconductor chip (see COMPUTER).

LONGITUDINAL WAVE (lŏn´ jĭ tōōd´n əl wāv) A longitudinal wave is a wave in which the particles of a material move parallel to the wave. Sound waves are longitudinal waves. They are produced by vibrating objects. The vibrating object causes the air molecules near it to vibrate. The molecules move backward and forward, producing a sound wave that moves outward from the object. The molecules move in the same direction that the wave is traveling.

A second kind of wave, called a transverse wave, occurs when particles move at right angles to the direction of wave travel. Water waves spreading across a pond are an example of transverse waves.

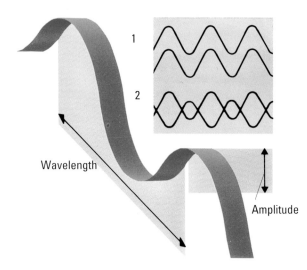

LONGITUDINAL WAVE

A longitudinal wave is described by its wavelength and amplitude. Two waves may be (1) in step (in phase) or (2) out of step (out of phase).

Both longitudinal and transverse waves can travel along a coiled spring (see TRANSVERSE WAVE).
See also SOUND; WAVE.

LOON A loon is any of four species of large water birds belonging to the family Gaviidae. Loons live only in the colder areas of the Northern Hemisphere. They are excellent swimmers. Loons are often called divers because they are able to dive as deep as 200 ft. [60 m] to catch fish. The loon has a thick neck and a pointed beak. Its webbed feet are set so far back on its body that they are excellent for swimming but almost useless for walking on land. Most loons spend the winters in or near the ocean. In the summer, they fly to northern inland lakes to breed (see MIGRATION). The female lays two or three eggs in a nest made of leaves and sticks. The nest is usually located near the edge of a body of fresh water. Both parents incubate the eggs until they hatch—about thirty days. Baby loons often ride on their parents' backs for several days or weeks before taking to the water themselves.

All loons, both male and female, have black wings and a black back with white spots in the breeding season. As winter approaches, this striking coloration fades to a somewhat duller gray without spots.

The common loon, or great northern diver, is

found along the North American coasts from close to the United States-Canada border to as far north as the Arctic Circle. It is about 3 ft. [90 cm] long. The red-throated diver is the smallest of the loons and reaches a length of about 2 ft. [60 cm]. Its throat is a chestnut red color during the summer. *See also* BIRD.

LOUDSPEAKER A loudspeaker is a device that is part of a radio receiver or a sound reproduction system. Loudspeakers convert electrical impulses into sound impulses and then amplify them. Loudspeakers are used in a wide range of sound reproduction systems, including televisions, cassette tape decks, compact disc players, public address systems, and concert systems.

The most common loudspeaker is the electrodynamic speaker. *Electrodynamics* refers to the effects produced from the interaction of electricity and magnets. In this speaker design, electrical impulses from a device, such as a microphone used during a concert or a compact disc player, are converted to sound by the attraction and repulsion of two magnetic fields. One magnetic field is produced by a

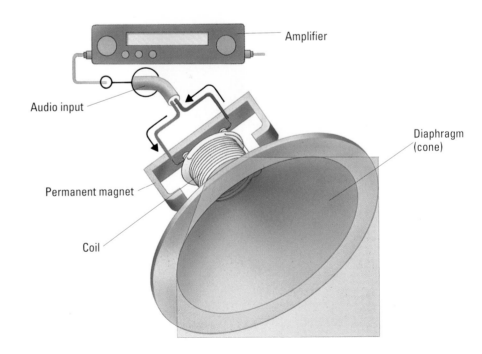

Amplifier

Audio input

Permanent magnet

Coil

Diaphragm (cone)

LOUDSPEAKER
A loudspeaker has a conical diaphragm with a coil wound around its base. The coil is located between the poles of a permanent magnet. Interaction between the magnetic fields of the coil and the magnet makes the diaphragm vibrate. The diaphragm's vibrations produce sound waves.

coil wrapped around the base of a cone-shaped device called a diaphragm. The other magnetic field is produced by a permanent magnet. The coil is connected to the permanent magnet by a circular device called a center pole piece. The strength of the impulses causes the coil to move toward and away from the permanent magnet. This motion causes the diaphragm to vibrate. The diaphragm sends these vibrations into the air. The cone shape of the diaphragm helps amplify (increase) the vibrations. The ear hears these vibrations as sound waves in the form of music or speech.

Other designs for loudspeakers include the piezoelectric and electrostatic. In piezoelectric speakers, electrical impulses are transmitted to the diaphragm through the vibration of a thin crystal (see PIEZOELECTRIC EFFECT). In electrostatic speakers, the diaphragm is usually made of a lightweight metal that is thin enough to vibrate (see ELECTROSTATICS). The diaphragm is mounted next to a metal plate. When electrical impulses pass through both magnetic fields (the diaphragm and the plate), electrical forces build up that cause the diaphragm to vibrate.

Most high-fidelity sound reproduction systems combine several types of speakers in order to reproduce the full frequency of sound (see FREQUENCY; SOUND). *High fidelity* refers to the reproduction of sound that is very similar to the original sound. The largest speakers, called woofers, most accurately reproduce low-frequency sound. Most woofers have diaphragms that are from 10 to 30 in. [25 to 76 cm] in diameter. The diaphragms of medium-sized speakers, called mid-range speakers, are from 4 to 8 in. [10 to 20 cm] in diameter. Mid-range speakers most accurately reproduce medium-frequency sound. The diaphragms of small speakers, called tweeters, are as small as 1 in. [2.5 cm] in diameter. Tweeters most accurately reproduce high-frequency sounds. A network of wires called a crossover channels the high-frequency, medium-frequency, and low-frequency sound impulses to the appropriate speakers.

Automobile sound systems, televisions, and portable radios often have a single mid-range speaker that must reproduce all frequencies.

Record players, cassette tape decks, and compact disc players often have woofers, mid-range speakers, and tweeters arranged in two or more boxes. These boxes can be positioned in a room so that the best sound is heard. Sound reproduction through two speakers in a single room is called stereophonic sound. Sound reproduction through four speakers in a single room is called quadraphonic sound.

Most loudspeakers are designed so that the sound projects only in one direction, which is usually forward. However, some loudspeakers are designed to be bidirectional, multidirectional, or omnidirectional. A bidirectional speaker projects sound in two directions—forward and backward. A multidirectional speaker projects sound in more than two directions. An omnidirectional speaker projects sound in all directions.
See also ELECTROMAGNETISM; SOUND RECORDING.

LOVEBIRD Lovebirds are small African parrots belonging to the genus *Agapornis* (see PARROT). Lovebirds are 4 to 6 in [10 to 15 cm] long and have bright green and yellow or orange feathers. Some of the nine species have a white ring around each eye. Like other parrots, lovebirds have short, curved bills

LOVEBIRD

Lovebirds can be recognized by their bright colors and short, rounded tails. Pictured here is Fischer's lovebird.

(usually red in color) and short tails. When making a nest, the female of some species carries grass and twigs to the nesting site in her rump feathers. The female lays four to six eggs, which hatch in about three weeks.

Lovebirds are so-called because they caress each other with their bills while courting and when perched and resting. They frequently imitate each other's actions or join together in song. A pair of lovebirds stays together for life.

LOWELL, PERCIVAL (1855–1916) Percival Lowell was an American astronomer. He was born in Boston, Massachusetts. He built the Lowell Observatory at Flagstaff, Arizona, in 1894 to study planets. Lowell was especially interested in Mars. He believed that there were canals on Mars that had been built by intelligent beings.

Lowell also predicted that there was another planet beyond Neptune. It was not until fourteen years after he died that the planet Pluto was actually seen. It was first seen by Clyde Tombaugh at the Lowell Observatory.

See also TOMBAUGH, CLYDE WILLIAM.

LUBRICATION (loo′ brĭ kā′ shən) Lubrication involves putting a substance between two surfaces so that the surfaces will slide past each other more easily. Such a substance is known as a lubricant. Lubrication reduces wear and friction.

There are many different types of lubricants, and each has different properties and uses. The main categories are liquid, oily lubricants; solid lubricants; and gaseous lubricants. Oil and other petroleum-based substances are the best-known liquid, oily lubricants. They are widely used because they offer good lubricating properties and protection against corrosion. They are also relatively cheap. Solid lubricants include soaps, minerals such as graphite and talc, polymer films such as Teflon, and waxes such as beeswax. The most common gaseous lubricant is air.

See also FRICTION.　　　　　**PROJECT 36**

LUGWORM The lugworm is any of several species of marine annelids belonging to the genus

Arenicola (see ANNELIDA). Lugworms have soft, segmented bodies and range in length from 4 to 16 in. [10 to 40 cm]. The front end of the body is often dark red and is thicker than the yellowish red rear end. Lugworms obtain oxygen through twelve or thirteen pairs of feathery red gills located along the middle segments (see GILLS). The middle and front segments also have bristles.

Lugworms live in intertidal areas (that is, between the low- and high-water marks) along the Atlantic coasts of North America and Europe. Some live in the Mediterranean Sea. Lugworms dig *U*-shaped tunnels in the sand. Some of these burrows are as deep as 2 ft. [60 cm]. At low tide, the burrows may be exposed. Lugworms rarely leave their burrows and constantly swallow sand and decayed organic materials. The sand is ejected through the anus and left in coiled heaps near the burrow, but the organic material is digested (see ANUS). Lugworms are sometimes called lobworms. They are popular as a bait for deep-sea fishing.

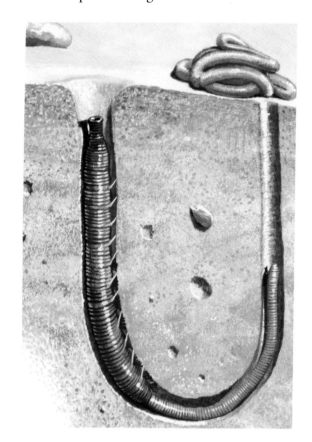

LUGWORM

Lugworms live in *U*-shaped tunnels in the sand of intertidal areas. They swallow sand and feed on the decayed organic material in it.

LUMBER

Lumber is the wood of trees sawed into logs and beams and otherwise prepared for its many uses. About 75 percent of the lumber produced in the United States is softwood and is used in buildings. Almost every house uses some lumber in its construction. Softwood is used to make thousands of other products, too. The remaining 25 percent is hardwood and is used mainly for furniture and floors.

In the production of lumber, a great deal of sawdust and small chips of wood is built up. However, this material is not wasted. Sawdust is used for fuel, insulation, and packing material. Pulp mills treat the chips with chemicals, making wood pulp. Pulp is used to make paper, plastics, and many other products.

TREE PLANTING
The forester (above) is planting tree seedlings that have been grown in a nursery.

Types of lumber The two main types of lumber are softwood and hardwood. Despite their names, these types are not based on the softness or hardness of the wood. They refer to the kind of tree from which the lumber came.

Hardwood comes from deciduous trees. Deciduous trees are those that lose their leaves in the fall, such as maples and oaks (see DECIDUOUS TREE). Many important hardwoods grow in the dense rain forests of the tropics. Such tropical hardwoods include mahogany, teak, rosewood, and ebony. Hardwood is used mainly for floors, furniture, paneling, and tools.

Conifers (mostly evergreen trees), such as pines, firs, and spruce, produce softwood lumber (see CONIFER; EVERGREEN). Softwood is used in construction and in making pulp. Plywood, used in construction, is made of several thin layers of softwood glued together. Softwoods provide most of the world's lumber.

prepared ground when the seedlings are between three and five years old. From the time the trees are planted to the time they mature, they require a great deal of attention. In the beginning, the trees must be kept clear of weeds. They must also be protected from animals, insects, fungi, and fire. The trees must be gradually thinned out as they grow, to allow the remaining trees more room to grow to full size.

Lumbering Logging is the first of three main branches of the lumber industry. Modern lumberjacks must be highly skilled in their work. Modern, large-scale lumbering operations require special mechanical equipment and technical knowledge.

The process of logging involves cutting down the trees, cutting them into logs, taking them out of the forest, and transporting them to the sawmills. The fellers, who cut down the trees, and the buckers, who cut the trunks into logs, use chain saws. These saws have a sawtooth cutting chain. This chain is driven rapidly around a steel blade by a small gasoline engine. The power saw that fellers use may weigh as much as 40 lb. [18 kg]. Such saws can slice through a tree trunk in a few seconds.

In cutting down a tree, the feller first makes an undercut. An undercut is a wedge-shaped chunk taken out of the tree trunk with an ax or power saw. The feller makes the undercut on the side of the tree he or she wants to fall toward the ground. The cut is made close to the ground to avoid wasting valuable wood and leaving a high stump. After the saw has cut about three-fourths of the way through the tree trunk, the tree loses its balance and falls toward the side of the undercut. Expert fellers can drop a tree exactly where they want it. Dropping a tree accurately, especially one that may be 200 ft. [61 m] tall, is considered an art. Next, the bucker trims the branches from the fallen trunk and cuts it into lengths of about 40 ft. [12 m] or shorter.

Next comes the process of extraction—that is, taking the lumber from where it has fallen to a central point called a landing. From there it is taken to the sawmill. If the landing lies near a road, trucks carry the logs to the mill. If it is on a railroad line, the logs are loaded onto flatcars for the trip. In the

TREE FELLING
Logging workers (above), called fellers, use power saws to cut down trees.

Raising the trees Foresters are the people who raise the trees to maturity. They advise the lumberjacks, also called loggers, which trees or which group of trees to fell (cut down). A logger is a worker who cuts down trees, saws them into logs, and brings them to the sawmill. Sometimes the foresters decide on block cutting, also called clear cutting, in which all the trees in a certain region of the forest are cut down when they have reached the right age. Then the area is replanted. Sometimes, nearly all the trees in a larger region of the forest are cut down, with a few "mother trees" left here and there to reseed the area of the forest naturally.

When foresters decide to replant the forest themselves, they use seedlings they have raised from seeds in a forest nursery. They plant the seedlings in

past, logs were bound into rafts and floated to the sawmill, but this is not common any more because many logging rivers have been dammed to produce hydroelectric power. Also, many forests now being harvested are not near rivers. There are also concerns that floating large cargoes of logs down river could cause pollution and also lead to clogging of rivers with debris.

From logs to lumber In fairly large sawmills, logs are kept in a pond until they go into the mill. The water protects the logs from insects, fungi, stain, and fire.

A moving conveyor chain carries the logs up a wooden chute into the mill (see CONVEYOR). Water forced through overhead pipes gives the logs a stinging bath. By the time the logs enter the mill, no sand, dirt, or small bits of metal remain on them that might dull the sharp saw blade. A moving platform called a carriage carries the logs into the teeth

LOG STORAGE
Thousands of logs float in this storage pond before they are cut into lumber.

of the first saw, called the headsaw. Each time the carriage goes past the saw, the saw slices off a board until the log is all cut. Moving belts then carry the boards, called green lumber, to the edger, a set of smaller saws. These saws trim the rough edges from each board and make the sides straight and even. A set of saws called the trimmer makes the ends of the boards square. It also cuts the boards to the required lengths and cuts off weak or bad spots.

Gang saws are used in some lumber mills, especially in Europe. In such mills, after the outer slabs of the logs are removed, the log moves into a set of straight-bladed saws. These saws cut the squared-up log into boards of the desired thickness in one operation.

The green lumber rides slowly on the green chain, which is a moving belt. Workers called graders test each board and decide its grade. They sort the boards according to size, quality, and type of wood. The boards are then stacked. They may be left for several months to dry. Sometimes, lumber is seasoned, which means removing excess moisture from the wood. More than half the weight of green lumber may be moisture in the wood. After seasoning, less than a tenth of its weight may come from moisture. A quick way of seasoning lumber is to put green lumber in heated buildings called dry kilns, in which the temperature of the air is gradually raised and the humidity lowered. Certain instruments tell how much moisture remains in the wood.

Instead of being cut into boards, logs may be used in other ways. They may be sliced very thinly to make veneer for manufacturing plywood or surfacing other pieces of lumber. Surface veneers, made from expensive, attractive hardwoods, are often glued to ordinary softwoods to make them look more attractive.

Shipping Most mills ship lumber to wholesale dealers. The wholesalers sell to retail lumberyards, to factories, and to construction companies. Most long-distance shipping is by rail or ship. Trucks make most of the shorter trips.

See also DEFORESTATION; FORESTRY; RAIN FOREST; WOOD.

LUMEN (lōō′ mən) A lumen is a unit that measures luminous flux. Luminous flux is the amount of light energy passing through an area per second. The intensity, or brightness, of a light is measured in units called candelas (see CANDELA; LIGHT). The lumen is the light striking a surface one meter square and one meter distant from a one candela source of light. *Lumen* is also a term used in anatomy. Lumen describes the inside space of a tubular organ, such as a blood vessel. In botany, *lumen* describes the space within the walls of a plant cell.

LUMINESCENCE (lōō′mə nĕs′ əns) Luminescence is the giving off of light by means other than heat (see INCANDESCENCE; LIGHT). An atom is

LUMINESCENCE
This watch has an electro-luminescent dial that glows with light when a button is pressed. The dial is powered by a small battery inside the watch.

made up of electrons moving around a central core called a nucleus (see ATOM). The electrons move around in orbits. Each orbit is a different distance from the nucleus. Electrons in a higher (farther) orbit have more energy than electrons in a lower (nearer) orbit. When radiation is applied to certain materials, their electrons absorb the energy and move into a higher orbit (see RADIATION). The electrons are said to be excited. At some point, the electrons give out the energy as light and drop back to their original orbits. This giving off of light is luminescence. If the light is given off by the electrons only while the radiation is applied, it is called fluorescence. If the light is given off by the electrons long after the radiation is removed, it is called phosphorescence (see FLUORESCENCE; PHOSPHORESCENCE).

There are several methods of producing luminescence. For example, luminescence occurs when an electric current is passed through a gas (see CURRENT, ELECTRIC). This happens in fluorescent lights. The electrons in the electric current collide with the atoms in the gas. These collisions cause the gas electrons to jump into higher orbits. The electrons then drop back down, and the gas glows. The inside of a television screen is coated with fluorescent substances. When a stream of electrons called a cathode ray is fired at them, they luminesce and form a picture.
See also CATHODE-RAY TUBE.

LUMINOSITY (lōō′ mə nŏs′ ĭ tē) The luminosity of a star is a measure of the total amount of energy emitted by the star per second (see STAR). The luminosity of a star depends upon its size and its temperature. If two stars are the same size, the hotter one will be the more luminous of the two. If two stars have the same temperature, the larger of the two will be more luminous. The sun, which is an average star, is often said to have a luminosity of 1 (see SUN). On this scale, some stars have a luminosity of 500,000. These stars give out 500,000 times more energy than the sun. Small white dwarf stars have a luminosity of 0.001 times that of the sun. The most luminous stars have the greatest absolute magnitude (see MAGNITUDE).

LUNG

Lungs are the organs through which oxygen gets into the body of a human being and other land-living vertebrates. Carbon dioxide also comes out of the body through the lungs.

Animals that live in water usually have gills instead of lungs (see GILLS). The lungs of land animals are like gills turned inside out. They have to be moist because dry gases will not go through animal tissues. They are spongy so that there is a lot of moist surface for the gases to pass through.

Human beings have two lungs. They fill the thoracic cavity (chest) on either side of the heart. The lungs are contained in a thin, tough membrane called the pleura. Below the lungs is a strong sheet of muscle called the diaphragm. When a person breathes in, the diaphragm and the muscles attached to the ribs make the chest expand. This makes the lungs expand so that air gets drawn in to fill them. The air comes in through the trachea (windpipe). This divides into two bronchi (singular: *bronchus*), with one going to each lung. In the lung, the tubes divide again and again into thinner and thinner tubes called bronchioles. At the end of each bronchiole is a cluster of round sacs. These are called alveoli (singular: *alveolus*), or air sacs. They have a rich supply of capillaries (tiny blood vessels) in their walls. It is here that the oxygen and carbon dioxide change places. Oxygen goes through the thin linings of the alveoli and capillaries into the blood at the same time as carbon dioxide comes out. There are about 600 million alveoli in human lungs, giving about 700 sq. ft. [65 sq. m] of breathing surface.

Different kinds of animals with lungs have somewhat different respiratory, or breathing, systems. For example, birds have especially efficient lungs that can be completely emptied of air. Reptiles and amphibians are cold-blooded and do not need as much energy as birds and mammals. Their breathing system is less efficient.

See also BREATHING; CIRCULATORY SYSTEM; RESPIRATION; RESPIRATORY SYSTEM. **PROJECT 64**

OXYGEN EXCHANGE

The tiny air sacs in the lungs, called alveoli, are surrounded by a network of tiny blood vessels called capillaries (below). Oxygen in the air first dissolves in a layer of moisture. It then passes into the capillary to be carried by the red blood cells.

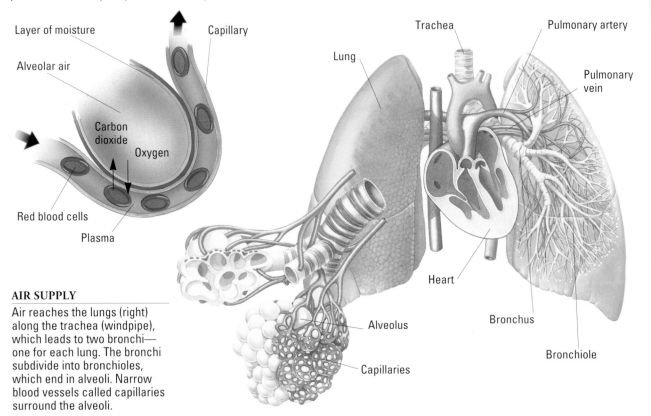

Layer of moisture

Capillary

Alveolar air

Carbon dioxide

Oxygen

Red blood cells

Plasma

Trachea

Pulmonary artery

Lung

Pulmonary vein

Heart

Alveolus

Bronchus

Bronchiole

Capillaries

AIR SUPPLY

Air reaches the lungs (right) along the trachea (windpipe), which leads to two bronchi—one for each lung. The bronchi subdivide into bronchioles, which end in alveoli. Narrow blood vessels called capillaries surround the alveoli.

LUNGFISH
An African lungfish can live for up to four years in the mucous cocoon it makes in the mud (right). It breathes through a hole at the top.

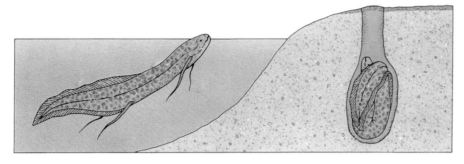

LUNGFISH A lungfish is a freshwater fish that belongs to the class Sarcopterygii. It is able to survive for long periods of time out of water because it can breathe air. When fish evolved, a saclike organ developed within their bodies. This organ became the swim bladder, which, in many fishes, is used to control buoyancy (see SWIM BLADDER). In the lungfishes, the swim bladder developed into a primitive lung (see LUNG). Lungfish can rise to the surface of water and gulp air to breathe. Because of this ability, lungfish are able to live in stagnant water with very little oxygen. The lungfishes do have gills, like other fishes, but these gills are poorly developed and some lungfishes will drown if they cannot get air from the surface (see GILLS). Scientists think that the lungfishes are similar to the ancient fishes that evolved into the air-breathing amphibians millions of years ago (see AMPHIBIAN; EVOLUTION).

There are four species of lungfishes in Africa, one species in South America, and one species in Australia. All six species live in hot regions. Often, a lake in which lungfish are living will dry up during the dry season. To survive during this time, the lungfish estivate. This is a type of hibernation (see HIBERNATION). The fish lie in a muddy, cocoonlike covering that has a breathing hole. This covering prevents them from drying up. When heavy rains refill the lake, the lungfish emerge to swim and feed.
See also FISH.

LUPINE (loo´ pən) Lupine is the name of a group of plants in the pea family, genus *Lupinus* (see PEA FAMILY). About a hundred kinds of lupines grow in North America. Some contain poisonous alkaloids (see ALKALOID). The seeds of others can be eaten. Lupines bear long, showy, spike-shaped clusters of flowers. The flowers are usually blue, yellow, red, or white. The leaves have several leaflets, arranged like the spokes of a wheel. Lupines are popular garden plants, and there are many cultivated varieties.

LUPINE
Lupines are colorful members of the pea family, grown for their tall spikes of flowers.

LYE Lye is a strong alkali, or a base that dissolves easily in water (see ALKALI; BASE). Lye is white and powdery. Its chemical name is sodium hydroxide (NaOH). It is also called caustic soda. Lye is made by the electrolysis of a solution of sodium chloride. Like other bases, lye neutralizes acids (see ELECTROLYSIS; NEUTRALIZATION).

Lye is often used in the home to clear clogged plumbing pipes. The base destroys wastes by eating into organic material. It is a very corrosive substance and must be used with great care.
See also CORROSION.

LYMPH (lĭmf) Lymph is a watery fluid in the body. It passes through body tissues carrying dissolved substances in it. Lymph—containing nutrients from food eaten, salts, and body regulating chemicals called hormones—passes out through the walls of blood vessels. It gradually gives up the substances that the cells need. At the same time, it picks up waste substances from the cells.

Lymph eventually drains into the lymphatic system and is returned to the bloodstream. It may carry white blood cells to a place where they are needed.

See also LYMPHATIC SYSTEM.

LYMPHATIC SYSTEM (lĭm făt′ ĭk sĭs′ təm) The lymphatic system is a network of tubes that carry lymph away from body tissues and back to

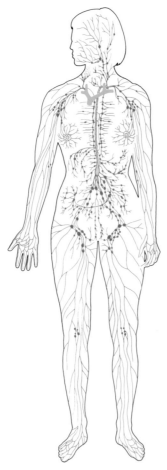

LYMPHATIC SYSTEM

The network of tubes that make up the lymphatic system reaches nearly all the parts of the body. The tubes carry a mixture of plasma and white blood cells called lymph, which returns to the blood along a vein (shown in blue) near the heart. Lymph nodes are found in the armpits, groin, and neck. They contain white blood cells that destroy bacteria to help fight infections.

the bloodstream (see LYMPH). In humans, lymph moves from small vessels called lymph capillaries to larger ones called lymphatics by the pressure of muscles as we walk and move. Valves keep the lymph going in the right direction. Eventually, all the lymph pours into two large lymphatics called trunks. They empty the lymph into the subclavian veins, which run under the collarbone, and thus back into the bloodstream. Lymph flows very slowly. About 3 pints [1.5 liters] return to the bloodstream in one day.

Along the larger lymph vessels, there are clusters of specialized tissue called lymph nodes. There are many of these in places such as the armpits, neck, and groin. The lymph drains into them easily. However, immune system cells, some of which are called lymphocytes, are located in the lymph nodes, and they filter out pathogens (disease-causing microorganisms) and impurities (see IMMUNITY; MICROORGANISM; PATHOGEN). Therefore, the lymph is cleaned as it passes back toward the bloodstream. When a person has a disease caused by a pathogen, his or her lymph nodes may become swollen and painful. This is because the nodes are working hard to destroy the pathogens. The spleen, thymus, and tonsils contain the same kind of tissue as lymph nodes.

See also CIRCULATORY SYSTEM; SPLEEN; TONSIL.

LYNX (lĭngks) The lynx is a member of the cat family, Felidae. Most lynxes are powerfully built and have stubby tails and long tufts of hair on their pointed ears.

The lynx is larger than a domestic cat, but smaller than leopards or mountain lions. Some lynxes weigh 45 lb. [20 kg], but most weigh from 15 to 25 lb. [6 to 11 kg]. Lynxes are found in parts of North America and Europe.

Lynxes live in forests or in rocky, bushy places. They hunt mainly at night. They feed on rabbits and other small animals. When their usual prey is scarce, lynxes may kill foxes and even deer. The female lynx bears from one to five babies in a litter.

The Canada lynx is the larger of two species that live in North America. The bobcat, which is the

LYNX
The lynx is a good climber that hunts mainly at night.

smaller North American lynx, lives mainly in the United States.

Lynxes are often hunted for their fur, which is light gray or grayish brown and spotted, and is long and silky.

See also CAT.

LYREBIRD (līr′ bûrd′) A lyrebird is a bird, about the size of a chicken, that lives in Australia. The lyrebird gets its name from the tail feathers of the male. These large and spreading feathers are arranged like a lyre, an ancient musical instrument. Two broad feathers curve upward, with slender and delicate feathers in between.

The tail of the lyrebird reaches its full length of about 2 ft. [61 cm] when the bird is about seven or eight years old. The male lyrebird normally carries its tail horizontally behind it, but displays its tail and sings to attract females during the mating season.

Apart from the tail, the two sexes are much alike. Both have a strong, melodious song. They can imitate the songs of other birds as well as mechanical sounds.

The lyrebird can fly, but rarely does so. It feeds entirely on the ground, where it finds worms, insects, and other small invertebrates. The lyrebird makes its nest on the ground. The nest is tightly woven and shaped like a dome. The female lays one egg in it.

See also BIRD.

LYREBIRD
The male lyrebird has a tail of large, spreading feathers arranged in the shape of a lyre, which is a harplike musical instrument.

M

MACAW (mə kô′) The macaw is a large parrot with very long tail feathers (see PARROT). Macaws live in the rain forests of Central and South America. There are eighteen different species of macaws.

The macaw has large, pointed wings and a short, but very powerful hooked beak. The macaw's body is covered with brilliantly colored feathers of green, yellow, blue, and red, depending on the species. The coloring is the same for both sexes. Macaws eat fruit, nuts, and seeds. These birds can be easily tamed and are sometimes kept as pets. However, their loud screams and the danger of their biting limit their popularity as pets. Nevertheless, several species are now quite rare as a result of being taken from the wild for the pet trade.

MACAW
The red and green macaw is a colorful parrot with a hooked beak. It lives in the rain forests of Central and South America.

MACH (mäk) The Mach is a unit of measurement for the speed of objects that fly at velocities close to or above the speed of sound. The unit is named in honor of Ernst Mach (1838–1916), an Austrian physicist and philosopher.

Mach numbers are used for the speeds of flying objects because the speed of sound in the air is not always the same. The speed of sound depends on the pressure (therefore, altitude) and the temperature of the air (see AIR). At sea level, at 32°F [0°C], sound travels at about 765 m.p.h. [1,232 kph]. The speed of sound decreases at higher altitudes. At 40,000 ft. [12,200 m], for example, sound normally travels at 660 m.p.h. [1,062 kph].

A Mach number is found by dividing the speed of an object by the speed of sound at the object's altitude. For example, the Mach number of an airplane flying at 740 m.p.h. [1,191 kph] at 40,000 ft. [12,200 m] is 740 divided by 660, or Mach 1.12. A plane traveling exactly at sound speed, or sonic speed, is therefore flying at Mach 1.

Flight slower than Mach 1 is called subsonic flight. Speeds close to or at the speed of sound are called transonic. Flight faster than Mach 1 is called supersonic flight (see SUPERSONIC FLIGHT). When the Mach number is greater than 5, the speed is referred to as hypersonic.

MACH
The Russian MiG-29 fighter can fly at a speed of Mach 2—at twice the speed of sound.

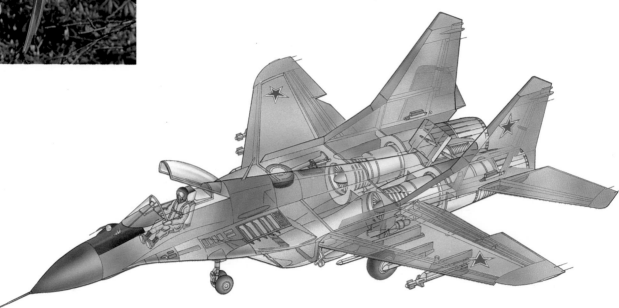

MACHINE, SIMPLE

A machine is a device that can do work. The work may be lifting an object; moving, crushing, or bending objects; and so on. Six different devices are generally recognized as simple, or basic, machines. These are the lever, the pulley, the wheel and axle, the inclined plane, the screw, and the wedge. By using these simple machines, people can perform tasks that they would not otherwise be able to do. For example, a pulley allows people to lift very heavy objects.

The six simple machines can be put together in various combinations to form other, more complicated machines. For example, a wheelbarrow is a combination of a lever and a wheel and axle. Suppose that the wheelbarrow contains a heavy object. The back of the wheelbarrow can be lifted off the ground, despite the weight. This is because the barrow acts like a lever and allows heavy objects to be lifted. A wheelbarrow also has a wheel and axle. This allows the object to be moved from place to place.

Two terms often used with regard to machines are *effort* and *load.* Effort is the force that is applied to the machine. Load is the force that the machine applies to the object (see LOAD). Without the machine, the effort would equal the load. With it,

the effort is usually much less than the load. A pulley, for example, allows much heavier weights to be lifted than can be lifted without a pulley. In this example, the load is the weight of the object being lifted. The effort is the force needed to pull the rope attached to the pulley. The ratio of the load to the effort is called the mechanical advantage of the machine (see RATIO). The mechanical advantage is almost always greater than one. This is because the load is almost always greater than the effort. For example, suppose a machine allows you to move a load with half the effort that would be needed with no machine. Then the mechanical advantage is the ratio 2:1.

Machines allow us to move heavier loads than we could on our own. However, this does not mean that we do less work. Work is closely related to energy (see ENERGY). The law of the conservation of energy says that the total energy in a system is constant. This means that the amount of energy in a system does not change unless energy is applied from outside. A simple machine does not create new energy, or work, by itself. For instance, a simple machine does a certain amount of work in moving a load. However, a person does work to use the machine. The work the person puts in equals the

WHEELBARROW
A gardener uses a wheelbarrow to move rotten apples. Wheelbarrows were among the earliest machines that used wheels.

work the machine puts out, less a small amount that is changed into heat in overcoming friction (see FRICTION).

Work is equal to the force times the distance over which the force is effective. If a person lifts an object, the work done to lift that object is equal to the object's weight times the distance that the object is raised. A simple machine allows a person to use less force, but the force that is applied must move through a greater distance. Suppose a pulley lifts a 22 lb. [10 kg] object through a distance of 9.8 ft. [3 m]. Suppose that the mechanical advantage of the pulley is 2:1. That means that only half as big a force as the weight of the object must be applied to the pulley to lift the object. However, the rope must be pulled through twice the distance the object moves, or 2 x 9.8 = 19.6 ft. [2 x 3 = 6 m]. Thus the work done, which is force times distance, is the same as what it would take to lift the object directly.

The ratio of the distances moved by the effort and the load is called the velocity ratio. The effort almost always moves through a greater distance than the load. Therefore, for most machines, the velocity ratio is greater than one. In a perfect machine, the velocity ratio equals the mechanical advantage. Then, all the effort goes into moving the load. In a real machine, there is always some energy loss. The mechanical advantage becomes less than the velocity ratio. The ratio of these two is called the efficiency of the machine. A perfect machine has an efficiency of one. A real machine has an efficiency of less than one. Most of the energy loss is due to friction. Work has to be done to overcome the friction. This reduces the mechanical advantage and so reduces the efficiency.

Lever, wheel and axle, pulley The simplest kind of lever has a bar, pivoted about a support. The support is called a fulcrum (see FULCRUM). Effort is applied to one part of the bar. The bar pushes the load at another part. There is only a very small energy loss in a simple lever. The bar bends a little under the effort, and this increases the amount of effort needed. Nevertheless, levers are very efficient machines.

There are three kinds of levers. A first-class lever has the effort and the load on either side of the fulcrum. A crowbar and a seesaw are examples of first-class levers. The mechanical advantage of this type of lever can be greater or less than 1:1. It depends on the distances of the load and the effort from the fulcrum. A second-class lever has the load between the fulcrum and the effort. Its mechanical advantage is always greater than 1:1. An example is a nutcracker or a wheelbarrow. A third-class lever has the effort between the load and the fulcrum. Its

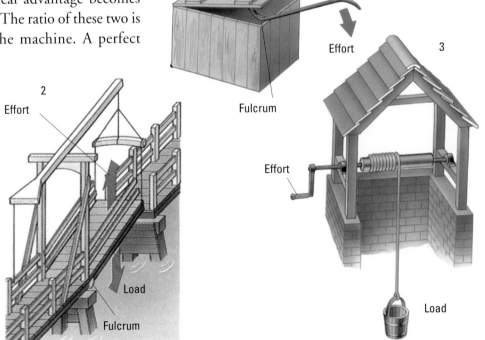

LEVERS AND WHEELS

A crowbar (1) is an example of a first-class lever, with the load and effort on opposite sides of the fulcrum (support). The simplest lift bridge (2) makes use of a third-class lever, with load and effort on the same side of the fulcrum. A wheel and axle, as in a windlass (3), also uses leverage when the crank (handle) is turned.

mechanical advantage is always less than 1:1. An example is a pair of sugar tongs (see LEVER).

In a wheel and axle, a rope is wound around an axle and attached to the load. The effort is applied to the edge of a large wheel attached to the axle. When it is turned once, the wheel moves through a large distance. However, the load only moves a short distance, because the axle is much smaller. The velocity ratio is the ratio of the diameters of the wheel and the axle. This is usually much greater than 1:1. Therefore, the mechanical advantage is large, and heavy loads can be lifted. Usually a handle (crank) is used instead of a wheel. The handle is pushed around in a circle. The wheel and axle system can be used to draw water from wells.

The pulley is similar to a wheel and axle. Pulleys are used in cranes and hoists. They have one or more wheels with rope running in grooves around the outside of the wheels. If there is just one wheel, the effort equals the load. This kind of pulley allows the direction of the load to be altered. Instead of lifting a weight upward, a person pulls downward on the rope. This is much easier to do. Two or more wheels can be used, with the rope running from one wheel to another. In this kind of pulley, the effort is less than the load. Such a pulley system is called a block and tackle.

Inclined plane, screw, wedge An example of an inclined plane is a board sloping from the back of a truck to the ground (see INCLINED PLANE). To lift a heavy object from the ground to the truck can be difficult. It is usually easier to push a heavy object up an inclined plane. The gentler the slope, the less effort is needed. Therefore, the mechanical advantage is greater. However, the object then has to be pushed farther. This increases the velocity ratio. Much of the effort goes into overcoming friction between the object and the plane. Friction can be reduced by moving the object on rollers.

An example of a screw is the screw jack used to "jack up" automobiles. With a screw jack, a very heavy truck can be lifted by one person. However, the handle of the jack has to be turned around many times. This means that the effort is being applied over a very large distance.

A wedge is similar to an inclined plane. Wedges are used, for example, to split wood. Force is applied to the thick end of the wedge. This drives the thin end of the wedge into the wood. The wood is forced apart and splits. An ax is a form of wedge.

PROJECT 50

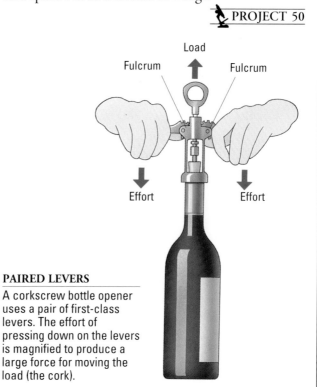

PAIRED LEVERS

A corkscrew bottle opener uses a pair of first-class levers. The effort of pressing down on the levers is magnified to produce a large force for moving the load (the cork).

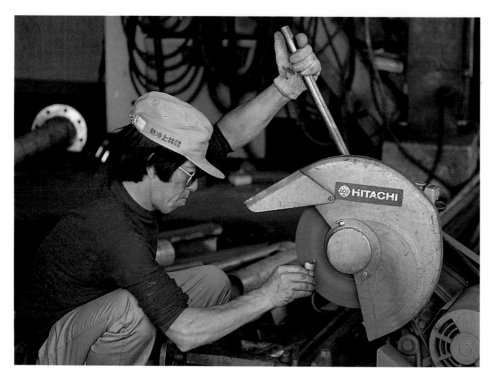

MACHINE TOOL
A worker uses a motor-driven grindstone to shape a piece of metal. This machine tool replaces the hand-held file, or rasp.

MACHINE TOOL A machine tool is a non-portable, power-driven machine used to shape or finish metal. The metal to be shaped can be in sheet, bar, or block form. It can be of any size, large or small. Different kinds of metal are often shaped by different types of machine tools. A machine tool is designed for automatic or semiautomatic operation. It performs repetitive tasks that would be very difficult or impossible to do by hand.

The most common use for machine tools is to make metal parts for other machines. Almost all metal parts in an automobile or aircraft are made with the help of machine tools. The operator of a machine tool is called a machinist. Some machine tools are small enough to be mounted on a work-bench. Others are as large as a two-story house. Each machine tool is designed for a specific kind of work, from threading wood screws to forming aircraft wing frames.

MACKEREL A mackerel is a saltwater fish that belongs to the family Scombridae. It is closely related to tuna (see TUNA). Mackerel swim in large schools, or groups, and are very fast swimmers.

There are seven species of mackerel found in the Atlantic and Pacific oceans. The Atlantic mackerel

MACKEREL
The common mackerel ranges throughout the North Atlantic Ocean and Mediterranean Sea. It has spiny fins and is caught as food for people.

is a popular game and food fish. It grows to about 20 in. [50 cm] in length. Most mackerel feed on surface plankton during the summer and on bottom-dwelling worms during the winter. The Atlantic mackerel, however, feeds on small crustaceans, such as shrimp, and on small schooling fishes.

See also CRUSTACEAN; PLANKTON.

MACROMOLECULE (măk′ rō mŏl′ĭ kyōōl′)
Macromolecules are very large molecules. Macromolecules consist of many small molecules joined end to end (see MOLECULE). The molecules of both natural and synthetic polymers are macromolecules (see POLYMER). Examples of natural macromolecules are proteins (made of amino acids joined together), carbohydrates (made of sugars), nucleic acids, and natural rubber. Many synthetic polymers, such as plastics, have industrial and medical uses. The substance hemoglobin, which gives blood its red color, is also a macromolecule.

See also NUCLEIC ACID; PLASTIC; PROTEIN; RUBBER.

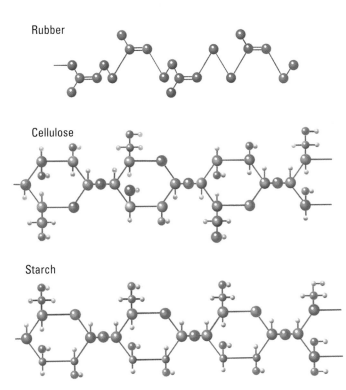

Rubber

Cellulose

Starch

MACROMOLECULE

Natural polymers made of macromolecules include rubber, cellulose, and starch.

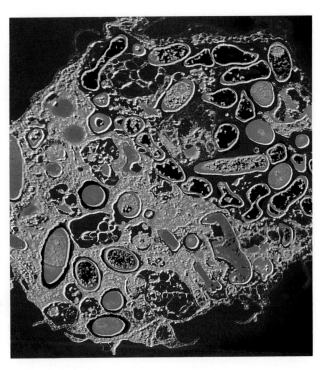

MACROPHAGE

This false-color electron microscope photograph (above) shows a macrophage that has engulfed a large number of bacteria.

MACROPHAGE (măk′ rə fāj′)
Macrophages are kinds of white blood cells that have very important functions in providing immunity (see IMMUNITY; LEUCOCYTE).

Macrophages are found especially in the liver, spleen, and lymph nodes, but also travel to other body tissues. They recognize and attack "foreign" particles and bacteria, ingest them by flowing around them, and destroy them by breaking them down with enzymes. This process is called phagocytosis.

Macrophages also stimulate the defensive cells of the immune system by presenting the "foreign" substances to them. They secrete several chemicals that help trigger inflammation and the immune response (see INFLAMMATION).

MAGMA
Magma is melted rock that forms within the earth. When magma solidifies, it forms igneous rock (see IGNEOUS ROCK).

Magma forms beneath the earth's crust where the temperatures range from 900°F to 2,500°F [482°C to 1,371°C]. The melted rock can be expelled from the earth's interior through

MAGMA
Magma is melted rock within the earth. When magma is expelled from a volcano or from a crack in the earth, it is called lava.

volcanoes and cracks in the earth's surface. Magma that reaches the earth's surface is called lava.
See also LAVA; VOLCANO.

MAGNESIUM (măg nē'zē əm) Magnesium (Mg) is a soft, silvery metallic element. It is one of the alkaline earth group of metals (see ALKALINE EARTH METAL; ELEMENT).

Magnesium was isolated by the British chemist Sir Humphry Davy in 1808 (see DAVY, SIR HUMPHRY). The element is found in the minerals dolomite and magnesite. Most magnesium is obtained by the electrolysis of molten magnesium chloride (see ELECTROLYSIS).

Magnesium is a very reactive metal. It burns in air with a dazzling white flame. Because of this, magnesium is used in flares, flashbulbs in photography, and fireworks. Magnesium also is used in a number of alloys (see ALLOY). Magnesium alloys are very light but strong. This makes them useful in aircraft and other vehicles and portable equipment. Magnesium alloys also resist corrosion (see CORROSION). For this reason, magnesium alloys are used to line water pipes and tanks.

Magnesium forms a number of important compounds (see COMPOUND). One such compound is magnesium oxide. Magnesium oxide is very resistant to high temperatures. Therefore, it is used to line furnaces for melting other metals. Two other important magnesium compounds are magnesium

hydroxide and magnesium sulfate. Magnesium hydroxide is used to relieve indigestion. When it is suspended in water, it is known as milk of magnesia. Magnesium sulfate is commonly known as Epsom salt. Epsom salt also has important medicinal uses (see EPSOM SALT).

The atomic number of magnesium is 12, and its relative atomic mass is 24.312. Its melting point is 1,200°F [649°C], and it boils at 1,994°F [1,090°C]. The relative density of magnesium is 1.7.

MAGNETIC FIELD A magnetic field is the place where a magnetic force can be detected. It occurs near a magnet or around a wire carrying an electric current. The magnetic field extends outward from the poles of a magnet. If another magnet is placed in the field, it is either attracted or repelled. A piece of iron in the magnetic field is attracted to the magnet.

A magnetic field can be represented by lines of force, which link the north and south poles of the magnet. The lines show the direction of the magnetic force in the field. The closer together the lines are, the stronger the magnetic force. Iron filings, scattered around a magnet, show the lines of force. The strength of a magnetic field is measured in units called tesla or gauss (see GAUSS). The earth's magnetic field is about 5×10^{-5} telsa. One tesla equals 10,000 gauss.
See also ELECTROMAGNETISM; FIELD; MAGNETISM.

PROJECT 28, 33, 37, 42

MAGNETIC LEVITATION VEHICLE

(măg nĕt′ ĭk lĕv′ ĭ tā′ shən vē′ ĭ kəl) A magnetic levitation vehicle, often called a maglev, is part of a modern high-speed transportation system. A maglev looks similar to a train, but it does not have wheels. Instead, it hovers over a tracklike device called a guideway. A maglev can travel up to 300 m.p.h. [483 kph]. A maglev is able to hover and move because of electromagnets and a linear electric motor (see ELECTROMAGNETISM; MAGNETISM).

American engineers James Powell and Gordon Danby designed the first superconducting maglev in the 1960s. Research in the United States continued into the mid-1970s, when funding from the U.S. government was cut. However, other countries, especially Germany and Japan, used this research as a basis to develop working maglev systems by the late 1980s. Renewed U.S. government funding in the early 1990s is resulting in increased interest in maglev in this country as well. The German design for maglev is able to hover because of electromagnetic attraction. Each car of the electromagnetic maglev has claws that fit around a steel guideway. Battery-powered electromagnets line the inside of the part of the claw that fits under the guideway. Electric current flowing to the electromagnets from the battery creates a magnetic field (see BATTERY; CURRENT, ELECTRIC).

The magnetic field causes the electromagnets to be attracted to the steel guideway. This attraction lifts the car about a $1/3$ in. [1.0 cm] off the guideway. Thick metal plates line the guideway. Wrapped around the plates are coils. The plates are actually the part of the linear electric motor called a stator. When electric current flows through the coils to the stator, a magnetic field is created. This magnetic field interacts with the magnetic field of the electromagnets. The interaction causes the train to be pushed and pulled forward. The engineer can increase or decrease the frequency of the electric current flowing through the linear electric motor to adjust the speed (see FREQUENCY).

One problem with the design of the German maglev is the heaviness of the electromagnets. This causes the cars to weigh over 100 tons [91 metric tons] each. Also, because the gap between the maglev car and the guideway is so small, the guideway must be very smooth and the electric current adjusted very precisely.

The Japanese design is slightly different from the German design. The Japanese maglev does not have claws. Instead, the magnets, which are made of a lightweight metal such as aluminum, line the bottom of each car. Magnets also line the guideway. The magnets work through repulsion rather than attraction. The magnets in each car are cooled by liquid helium (see HELIUM). When the magnets reach a supercool state, they lose all resistance to electrical current. They become superconductors (see SUPERCONDUCTIVITY). This causes the magnets in the car to very powerfully repel the magnets in the guideway, allowing the maglev to ride 3 to 6 in. [7.62 to 15.24 cm] above the guideway. This gap means the Japanese system does not need as smooth a guideway or as precise amounts of electric current as the German system. The use of lightweight magnets means the Japanese cars weigh almost 17 tons [15 metric tons] less than the German cars. However, the larger gap means the Japanese maglev handles curves poorly, and stopping and starting tends to be bumpy. Also, the superconducting magnets are more expensive than conventional electromagnets.

Some engineers predict that high-speed maglev trains will eventually replace airline routes between places that are less than 500 mi. [804 km] apart. For example, a maglev system linking New York City and Boston, Massachusetts, by way of Albany, New York, has been proposed. The maglev would take only about 2 hours to travel 360 mi. [580 km]. In addition, a demonstration maglev line running from Orlando Airport to nearby Disney World in Orlando, Florida, has been proposed. Officials in California, Washington, D.C., and Germany are also considering maglev systems. It is hoped the use of maglevs will lessen air-traffic congestion.

MAGNETIC POLE

The magnetic poles of a magnet are those parts where magnetism seems to be concentrated (see MAGNETISM). A magnet has two different poles, called a north pole and a south pole. Since unlike poles attract each other, the

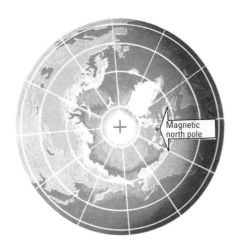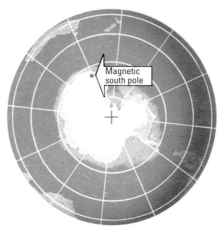

MAGNETIC POLE
The magnetic north pole is near Prince of Wales Island in northern Canada. The magnetic south pole is in Wilkes Land in Antarctica.

north pole of one magnet attracts the south pole of another magnet. The north poles of two different magnets repel each other, or push each other away.

The earth acts like a huge magnet. People use this fact in navigation with a compass (see COMPASS; NAVIGATION). In a compass, a magnet is pivoted in a glass case. The north pole of the magnet points toward the north. Since unlike poles attract each other, this shows that the magnetic pole in the Northern Hemisphere is really the south pole of a magnet (see MAGNETIC FIELD).

The magnetic pole of the Northern Hemisphere is called magnetic north. It is located about 1,000 mi. [1,600 km] from the geographic North Pole. The magnetic pole of the Southern Hemisphere, called magnetic south, is located about 1,500 mi. [2,400 km] from the geographic South Pole. The magnetic declination is the angle between the directions of the magnetic and geographic poles. The earth's magnetic poles shift slightly from year to year, causing a change in the angle of declination.　　　　**PROJECT 42**

MAGNETIC RESONANCE IMAGING
(măg nĕt´ ĭk rĕz´ ə nəns ĭm´ ĭj ĭng) Magnetic resonance imaging, also called MRI, is a diagnostic procedure that uses a large magnet, radio frequencies, and a computer to create images of the body's internal structures. MRI is used in cases in which X rays cannot produce an image (see X RAY).

The images produced by MRI are detailed sections of the anatomy. One of the tremendous advantages of MRI is that it can show views of the patient's internal organs from a variety of angles. The resulting images may be called axial, sagittal, or coronal views, depending on the angle.

MRI is useful in examining the head, neck, and spine. It also is useful in diagnosing bone, joint, and muscle disorders; tumors (abnormal growths); and certain heart and blood vessel diseases. MRI examinations are performed by technologists. The images are reviewed and interpreted by radiologists—physicians who specialize in the use of radiation for diagnosis and treatment.
See also RADIOLOGY.

MAGNETIC STORM
A magnetic storm is a disturbance in the magnetic field of the earth. Magnetic storms are caused by solar flares. Solar flares are violent eruptions on the sun's surface that seem to be associated with sunspot activity (see SUNSPOT). Solar flares make the solar wind stronger. The solar wind is a stream of charged particles (electrons and protons) moving from the sun through outer space at speeds of more than 435 mi. [700 km] per second. These particles cause disturbances in the earth's magnetic field.

Magnetic storms prevent compass needles from working correctly. They also disturb radio transmissions. The concentration of charged particles near the poles during magnetic storms creates a magnificent display of shimmering light in the night sky. These lights are referred to as auroras.
See also AURORA; MAGNETISM; SOLAR WIND.

MAGNETISM

Magnetism is the force that acts between magnets. People have recognized the properties of magnets for thousands of years. Around 800 B.C., the Greeks discovered that pieces of lodestone, which is a rock made of iron oxide, attracted each other. Later, the Chinese used lodestone in making the first compass. They hung a piece of lodestone on the end of some string and noted how the lodestone moved. One end always pointed north and the other end pointed south. The Chinese realized that they could use the properties of the lodestone to determine direction (see COMPASS; LODESTONE).

The next discovery regarding magnetism came in 1600. In that year, the English scientist Sir William Gilbert realized that the earth was a giant magnet (see GILBERT, SIR WILLIAM). Gilbert's discovery helped people understand why lodestones and other magnets point toward the earth's geographic North Pole (see MAGNETIC POLE).

In the late 1800s and early 1900s, scientists came to realize that magnetism is usually caused by moving electrons. All matter is made up of atoms (see ATOM). Each atom has a central core called a nucleus. Small charged particles, called electrons, orbit the nucleus. Electrons also rotate. When charged particles, such as electrons, move, they create a magnetic field. Sometimes, the magnetism that results from the motion of the different electrons in each atom cancels out. Then the material is nonmagnetic. In other materials, however, the magnetism that results from movement of the different electrons does not cancel out. Then the material is capable of being magnetized.

Magnets Magnetism occurs most strongly in three metals: iron, cobalt, and nickel. These metals can be used to make strong magnets. Iron is almost always used in making magnets, because it is the cheapest of the three metals. Often, magnets are made of steel, an alloy of iron (see ALLOY; STEEL).

The two ends of a magnet are called the north pole and the south pole. The north pole of a magnet points generally toward the geographic North Pole of the earth when the magnet is suspended. Similarly, the South Pole of a magnet generally points towards the geographic South Pole of the earth.

If two like poles of a magnet are brought close together, they repel each other. For example, the north poles of two magnets repel each other. Opposite poles attract each other. Since magnets can affect each other without touching, they are

MAGNETIC ATTRACTION

Magnets attract metals that can become magnets, such as iron and its alloys. Steel paper clips and tacks held by the magnet become magnets themselves and attract yet more paper clips and tacks.

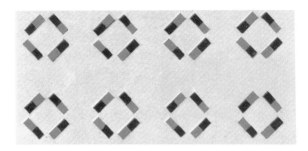

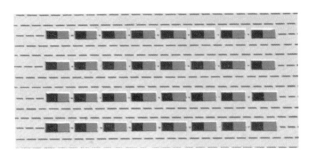

MAGNETIC DOMAINS

When a ferromagnetic metal such as iron is unmagnetized (above left), the north and south poles of the domains attract each other, and as a whole, cancel out the magnetism. When the metal is magnetized (above right), the domains are arranged in lines, creating a powerful magnetic field.

said to have a magnetic field (see MAGNETIC FIELD). The magnetic field extends outward from the poles of the magnet. If another magnet is placed in this field, it is either attracted or repelled.

Iron filings, which are small pieces of metal, can be used to show the lines of force in the magnetic field around a magnet. To show these lines of force, the magnet is placed underneath a piece of cardboard. The iron filings are then scattered over the cardboard and gently shaken about. The iron filings line up along the lines of force. These lines of force extend from each pole of the magnet. As they move away from the poles, they spread out.

There are many ways to make a magnet. If a magnet is placed near a piece of iron, the iron becomes magnetized. Stroking a piece of iron with one end of a magnet also magnetizes the iron. The second method produces a stronger magnet. Iron can also be magnetized by using electricity. This is done by winding a coil of wire around a piece of iron. An electric current is passed through the wire. The current causes the iron to become magnetized. When the current is shut off, the iron loses its magnetism. This effect is used in large, powerful magnets called electromagnets (see ELECTROMAGNETISM).

Some materials, such as hard steel and certain other iron alloys, are very difficult to magnetize. Once they are magnetic, they are just as difficult to demagnetize. Their magnetism is called permanent magnetism. Ordinary magnets are permanent magnets. Soft iron gains and loses magnetism easily. This is called temporary magnetism. Soft iron is used in certain electromagnets where the magnetism needs to be turned on and off.

Ferromagnetism There are different kinds of magnetism. For example, the metal bismuth is repelled by any magnetic field. This kind of magnetism is called diamagnetism. The most important kind of magnetism is ferromagnetism. Ferromagnets are strongly magnetic. Iron, cobalt, and nickel are the only ferromagnetic elements. Ferromagnetic materials are made up of many thousands of small magnets called domains. Normally, different domains point in different directions. Their magnetic fields cancel out, and the material is not magnetic. When the material is magnetized, the domains line up and point in the same direction. The magnetic fields of the domains combine to give a powerful magnetic field. When a magnet is demagnetized, the domains again point in different directions. A magnet can be demagnetized if it is heated, dropped, or struck with force.

PROJECT 28, 33, 42

ACTIVITY *How to show magnetism*

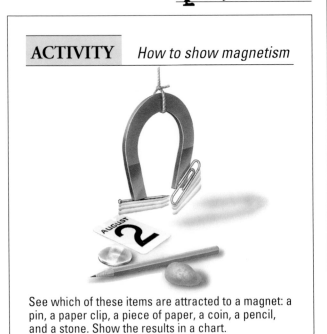

See which of these items are attracted to a magnet: a pin, a paper clip, a piece of paper, a coin, a pencil, and a stone. Show the results in a chart.

MAGNETITE Magnetite is a black, metallic mineral made of iron oxide (Fe_3O_4). Magnetite is an important iron ore—that is, a mineral from which iron is extracted. Some forms of magnetite, especially lodestone, are powerful natural magnets (see LODESTONE; MAGNETISM; MINERAL).

Magnetite is found in scattered crystals (and sometimes in large masses) in igneous and metamorphic rocks (see CRYSTAL; IGNEOUS ROCK; METAMORPHIC ROCK). Grains of magnetite found in rocks give an indication of the positioning of the rocks when they were formed. The study of the magnetism in these grains provides information on the earth's magnetic field in prehistoric times. This field of study, called paleomagnetism, is important in research into continental drift and the magnetism of the earth.

See also CONTINENTAL DRIFT.

MAGNETO (măg nē´ tō) A magneto is a device used to make a spark in some internal combustion engines. In a piston internal combustion engine, a mixture of fuel and air is passed into a cylinder. The mixture is then ignited by a spark created by a magneto. The mixture burns, producing hot gases. These hot gases push the piston down the cylinder (see ENGINE). Magnetos are used in lawn mowers, motorcycles, and most aircraft that have internal combustion engines. They were also used in early automobiles but are not used in modern ones.

A magneto contains a magnet and a conductor made of two coils of wire wound around a piece of iron. One coil has only a few turns of wire. It is called the primary coil. The other has many turns and is called the secondary coil. Either the coil or the magnet is spun around, while the other is kept still. This induces an alternating electric current in the primary coil (see ALTERNATING CURRENT; ELECTROMAGNETISM; INDUCTION).

The primary coil is connected to a device called a contact breaker. When the alternating current reaches a peak, the contact breaker opens and stops the current from flowing. The sudden change in strength of the current in the primary coil induces an electric current in the secondary coil. Because the secondary coil has many more turns of wire

than the primary coil does, the induced potential difference, or voltage, is very large in the secondary coil (see POTENTIAL). The high voltage produces a large current. This current flows to the spark plug to produce a strong spark.

Magneto ignition is simple and cheap, but this system does not work very well for starting a large engine, such as an automobile engine. Therefore, in modern automobiles, the magneto ignition system has been replaced by the battery ignition system. *See also* AUTOMOBILE.

MAGNETOMETER (măg´ nĭ tŏm´ ĭ tər) A magnetometer is an instrument that measures the strength of a magnetic field (see MAGNETIC FIELD). Magnetometers are often used to detect variations in the earth's magnetic field. These variations help scientists find deposits of certain natural resources, such as iron and nickel.

A simple magnetometer consists of a wire coil that produces an electric voltage when passed through a magnetic field. The size of this voltage gives a measurement of the strength of the magnetic field.

See also MAGNETISM; POTENTIAL; VOLT.

MAGNIFICATION (măg´ nə fĭ kā´ shən) Magnification is the apparent enlargement of an object when viewed through certain optical

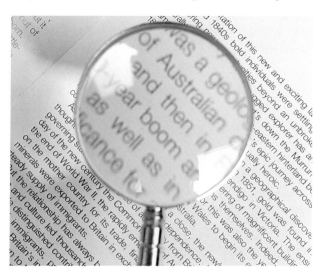

MAGNIFICATION—Magnifying glass

These letters look about three times as big when viewed through a magnifying glass. The magnification of the glass is therefore about x3.

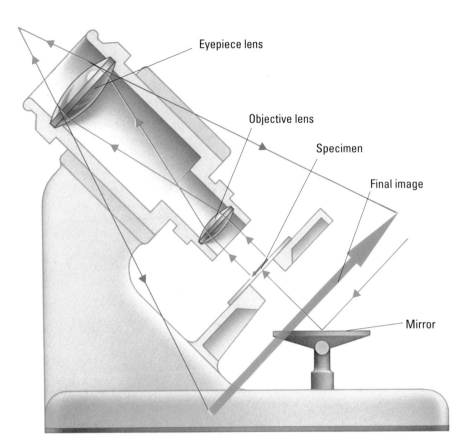

Eyepiece lens

Objective lens

Specimen

Final image

Mirror

MAGNIFICATION—
Microscope
The magnification of a
compound microscope is
found by multiplying the
magnifying power of the
objective lens by the
magnifying power of the
eyepiece lens.

instruments, such as a microscope, a telescope, binoculars, or a magnifying glass. The magnification of an object can be described as the increase in apparent area of the object or as the increase in the apparent length of its sides. Magnifications are usually given as the increase in linear dimension (length of a side). A pair of binoculars with a magnification of x10 makes the length of an object's side appear to be 10 times larger than it is when seen by the naked eye. Therefore, the object appears to be 10 times nearer than it really is. This is equal to an area magnification of 10^2 or 100 times.

See also BINOCULARS; MICROSCOPE; TELESCOPE.

MAGNITUDE Magnitude is a measurement of the brightness of a star or other heavenly body as we see it from Earth. In ancient times, stars visible to the unaided eye were classified into six magnitudes. The brightest stars in the sky were of first magnitude, while the faintest stars were of sixth magnitude.

The ancient system of magnitude has been slightly revised by modern astronomers. Today, a star of any magnitude is 2.5 times brighter than a star of the next magnitude. Thus, a star whose magnitude is 1 is 2.5 times brighter than a star whose magnitude is 2. The modern magnitude scale extends both forward and backward to include stars that are very faint and those that are extremely bright. Using large telescopes, astronomers can see some stars so faint that their magnitude is greater than 20. Some very bright stars have negative values of magnitude. The brightest star in the night sky, Sirius, has a magnitude of -1.4. The sun has a magnitude of -27.0.

These magnitudes are referred to as apparent magnitude. Absolute magnitude measures the brightness of a star in comparison with other stars. In order to do this, astronomers must determine how bright each star would be at the same distance away from the earth. Astronomers define this distance as 32.6 light-years (10 parsecs) (see LIGHT-YEAR; PARSEC). For example, if the sun were 32.6 light-years away from the earth, it would have a magnitude of 4.8. Hence, the sun has an absolute magnitude of 4.8. The absolute magnitude of Sirius is 1.3.

See also ASTRONOMY; STAR.

MAGNOLIA FAMILY

Magnolias are often grown as ornamental trees in parks and gardens. Originally native to Asia and North America, they are now grown in many parts of the world.

MAGNOLIA FAMILY The magnolia family includes 12 genera (plural of *genus*) with over 200 species of dicotyledonous flowering trees and shrubs (see DICOTYLEDON). Magnolias have alternate, simple leaves, and large, single flowers growing at the ends of the branches. The flowers have many stamens and pistils and usually six to fifteen petals (see FLOWER; LEAF). The seeds hang by threads from conelike fruits.

The southern magnolia grows throughout the southeastern United States. This evergreen species is prized for its large white flowers. The big-leaf magnolia is a deciduous species and has the largest flowers and the largest undivided leaves of any tree native to the United States. The flowers are about 10 in. [25 cm] across. The leaves measure about 30 in. [75 cm] long by 10 in. [25 cm] wide. Tulip trees, common in the United States, also belong to the magnolia family.

MAGPIE The magpie is a bird belonging to the crow family, Corvidae. Magpies are found in North America, Mexico, Europe, and Asia. Their long tail feathers make them easy to identify at a distance.

Magpies eat all kinds of food, including the eggs of other birds. Their nests are made of twigs cemented together with mud and are unusual because the opening is at the side rather than the top. For protection, the magpie often places its nest in thorny bushes. The female lays five to ten grayish white, brown-spotted eggs. Magpies usually travel in groups. They can imitate various other

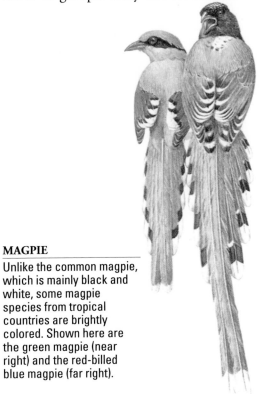

MAGPIE

Unlike the common magpie, which is mainly black and white, some magpie species from tropical countries are brightly colored. Shown here are the green magpie (near right) and the red-billed blue magpie (far right).

bird calls. Some magpies have been tamed and taught to speak simple syllables.

The black-billed magpie lives in various sections of North America, Europe, and Asia. This species is black, with white feathers on the underparts and wing tops. The yellow-billed magpie lives only in California.

MALACHITE (măl′ ə kīt′) Malachite is a bright green mineral from which copper is taken (see MINERAL). Malachite is a copper carbonate that contains water. The mineral frequently forms in layers that range in color from apple green to dark gray green. Sources of this mineral include Russia, Britain, Africa, Australia, and the United States (Arizona).

Malachite is used chiefly to make jewelry, other ornaments, and mosaics. In ancient times, people made bracelets of malachite. It was believed that such bracelets gave protection against disease, lightning, and spells cast by witches.

MALACHITE

Malachite is a beautifully banded, bright green mineral from which copper is taken. Malachite has been used to make jewelry since ancient times.

MALARIA (mə lâr′ ē ə) Malaria is one of the most widespread, serious diseases in the world. It is caused by a parasite. The parasitic organism is a one-celled protozoan that belongs to the family Plasmodiidae and the genus *Plasmodium* (see PARASITE; PROTO-ZOA). There are four species of *Plasmodium* that infect humans, causing malaria. There are over fifteen species that cause the disease in other verte-brates (animals with backbones). The *Plasmodium* protozoan lives in the red blood cells of the host

animal. The protozoans eventually destroy the red blood cells, weakening the host (see BLOOD).

A person who has malaria suffers from spells of fever and chills. After a few days, the person may seem to recover, but the fever spells soon return. If the disease goes untreated, the cycle can continue for months. Antimalarial drugs, such as quinine, can help prevent the disease. These same medicines are also used to treat malaria once a person is infected (see QUININE).

Malaria is spread by mosquitoes. A mosquito bites an infected animal and sucks up some of the larvae of the *Plasmodium* protozoan, which live in the infected animal's blood (see LARVA). When the mosquito bites another animal, the *Plasmodium* larvae enter the blood of the new animal and infect it. The animal comes down with the disease malaria.

Malaria originally occurred throughout much of Africa, Southeast Asia, Central America, Asia, South America, parts of Europe, and the eastern half of the United States. However, people have been successful in eliminating malaria in many parts of the world. Africa, South America, and Southeast Asia still have widespread malaria. Malaria can be treated and cured with drugs, but the best way to fight it is to kill the mosquitoes that spread the disease. The use of insecticides has been successful in many places (see INSECTICIDE). The elimination of malaria in parts of Southeast Asia helped the United States defeat the Japanese during World War II (1939–1945). Until that time, nearly one-fourth of all hospital patients during previous wars in the region were sick with malaria.

MALE Most animal species have two separate sexes—the male and the female (see FEMALE). Whether an animal is a male or a female depends on the genes and chromosomes in its cells (see CHROMOSOME; GENE). When animals mate, the male's sperm fertilizes the egg or eggs of the female. This sexual reproduction results in a mixing of genes from the male and female parents. It causes a greater variety of characteristics in the offspring. The greater variety increases the chances that at least some of the offspring will survive (see NAT-URAL SELECTION).

In many species the male and female look alike, but the male is quite often larger and more powerful than the female. He may use his strength to defend his mate and family against enemies. He may also fight other males for the right to occupy a given area or to control a group of females. Males are often more colorful than females, especially among birds, and they use their colors to attract mates. Most animal species produce the two sexes in more or less equal numbers. In some species, however, the males are much scarcer than females.

Most plant species have both male and female parts in the same flower. Some plants have separate male and female flowers, or even separate male and female plants.

MALLEABILITY (măl′ ē ə bǐl′ĭ tē) Malleability is the capacity of a material to be hammered or rolled into thin sheets. Gold is one of the most malleable of metals. It can be easily beaten into sheets that are so thin, they become translucent (permitting light to pass through). Other metals noted for their malleability are silver, copper, aluminum, tin, zinc, and lead.

Some of the malleable metals, such as silver, aluminum, and copper, can also be drawn out into very fine wire without breaking. This property is known as ductility (see DUCTILITY; WIRE). Any metal, even the almost unmalleable cast iron, becomes more malleable when it is heated.

MALLOW FAMILY The mallow family includes about seventy-five genera (plural of *genus*) containing about a thousand species of annual and perennial plants. They may be herbaceous plants, shrubs, or trees (see ANNUAL PLANT; HERBACEOUS PLANT; PERENNIAL PLANT). Most are tropical. The leaves may be lobed or divided and may have smooth or toothed margins (see LEAF). Frequently, tiny hairs cover the leaves, stems, and even the blossoms.

Mallow flowers are usually large and brightly colored. They have five petals and five sepals. The flowers are usually perfect—that is, they contain both stamens and pistils (see FLOWER). Pollination is usually done by insects, though the flowers may fertilize themselves (see POLLINATION). Economically, the most important member of the mallow

MALLOW FAMILY
Common mallow has tall stalks of pink flowers. It usually grows near water.

family is cotton. Other members include okra, hollyhock, and hibiscus.

MAMBA (măm′ bə) The mamba is a poisonous African snake that belongs to the family Elapidae. It is related to the cobra (see COBRA). Mambas have fangs in the front of their mouth. The fangs have a groove down the back of them, and poisonous venom flows down this groove. The venom of a mamba can kill a person in twenty minutes. The black mamba, largest of all mambas, grows 14 ft. [4.2 m] long. It lives on the ground. The green mamba is smaller and lives in trees. Mambas eat small mammals, birds, and lizards.

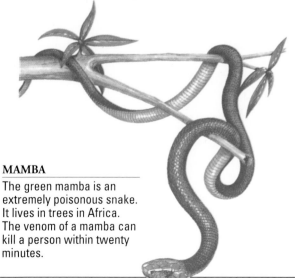

MAMBA
The green mamba is an extremely poisonous snake. It lives in trees in Africa. The venom of a mamba can kill a person within twenty minutes.

Mammal

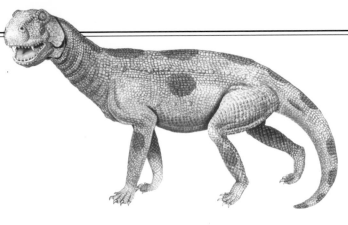

A mammal is a warm-blooded, vertebrate animal that belongs to the class Mammalia (see VERTE-BRATE; WARM-BLOODED ANIMAL). Two distinguishing characteristics of mammals are these: the females have mammary glands, which produce milk for the young; and mammals have hair covering all or parts of their body.

There are about 4,400 living species of mammals. They range in size from the 2 in. [5 cm] long pygmy white-toothed shrew to the 105 ft. [31 m] long blue whale, the largest animal on Earth.

Mammals evolved from reptiles about 200 million years ago (see EVOLUTION; REPTILE). The

ANCESTOR OF MAMMALS
The therapsid was a reptile that lived 230 million years ago. Its bone structure showed many mammallike features.

first mammals were very small—about the size of mice. As time went on, many more species of mammals evolved.

Monotremes

Marsupials

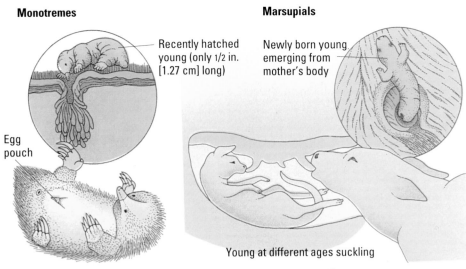

Recently hatched young (only 1/2 in. [1.27 cm] long)

Egg pouch

Newly born young emerging from mother's body

Young at different ages suckling

TYPES OF MAMMALS
Monotremes, such as the echidna (far left), are primitive mammals that lay eggs. The marsupials (left) include kangaroos and wallabies. They give birth to underdeveloped young, which continue their development in the mother's pouch. In placental mammals such as the rabbit (bottom left), the young develop fully in the mother's womb before being born.

Placentals

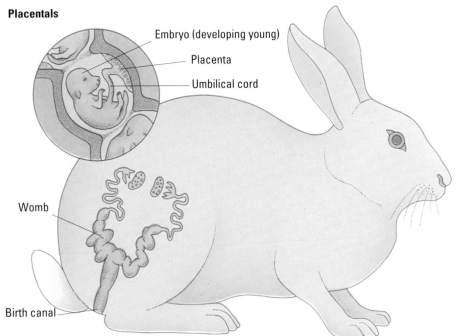

Embryo (developing young)

Placenta

Umbilical cord

Womb

Birth canal

MAMMAL EVOLUTION
The evolutionary history of mammals is shown in the diagram (right). The earliest mammals date from Jurassic and Cretaceous times, more than 65 million years ago. They were small creatures resembling shrews. They evolved rapidly so that there was a great variety by Eocene times. Over years of geological time, many mammals became extinct (shown as black silhouettes). Today's mammal types are shown at the top of the diagram.

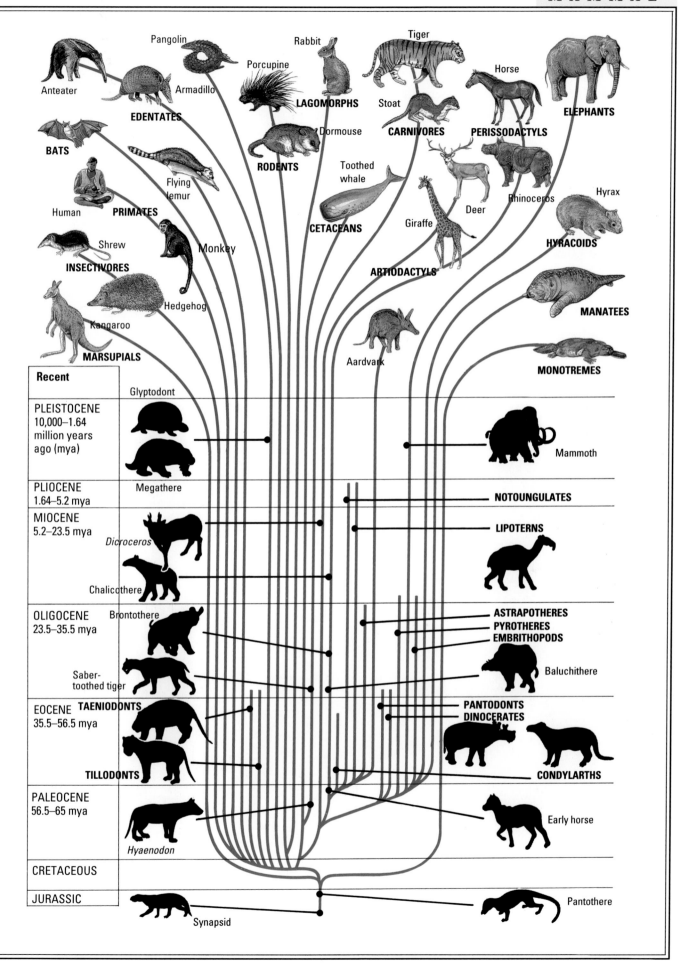

There are three main groups of mammals, each of which reproduces differently (see REPRODUCTION). The monotremes are the most primitive of all mammals. They lay eggs, but when the young hatch, they feed on their mother's milk like all other mammals. The platypus is an example of a monotreme (see MONOTREME; PLATYPUS). The marsupials give birth to their young before the babies have fully developed. The babies crawl into a pouch on their mother's belly. They feed on milk, stay warm and protected, and finish developing while in the pouch. The kangaroo and the opossum are examples of marsupials (see KANGAROO; MARSUPIAL; OPOSSUM). Most mammals alive today are placentals. The young develop while still inside the mother and are nourished by the mother's blood through an organ called the placenta (see PLA-

CENTA). In this way, the babies obtain food and oxygen without actually eating or breathing.

Mammals care for their young much longer than any other animal. Most animals—such as insects and turtles—never care for their young. They lay their eggs and leave. Most mammals, on the other hand, care for their young until the young can protect themselves. This extra protection helps the young mammals survive during the most dangerous period of their lives. Because of this parental care, mammalian young have a high survival rate. Therefore, mammals, unlike other types of animals, give birth to fewer young each year. In contrast with fish and reptiles, many of which lay hundreds or millions of eggs each year, most mammals give birth to fewer than ten young a year. *See also* ANIMAL KINGDOM.

MAMMAL VARIETY
Mammals come in all shapes and sizes. Shown here are (1) a woolly opossum from South America and (2) a bowhead whale of the Arctic and Antarctic oceans. The opossum is a marsupial. The bowhead whale is a placental mammal.

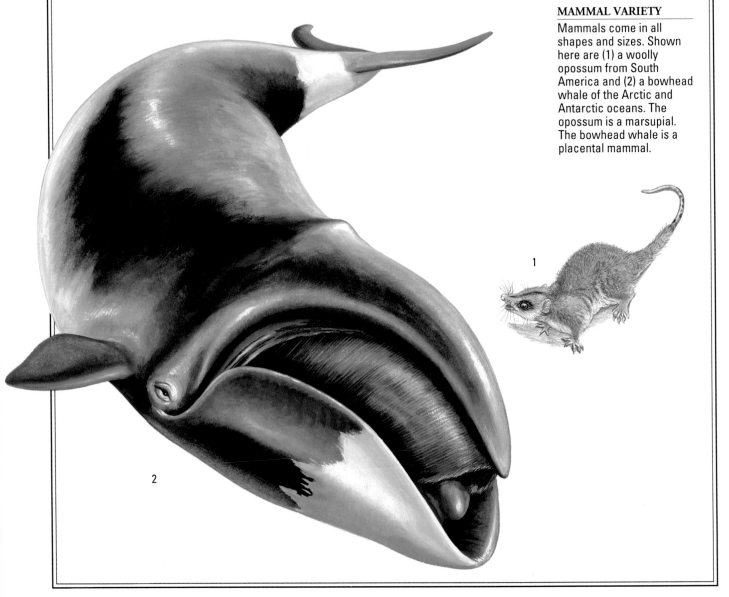

MAMMOTH Mammoths are an extinct genus of the elephant family, Elephantidae. The best-known of the mammoths is the woolly mammoth (*Mammuthus primigenius*). Mammoths are closely related to mastodons, an older genus of elephant-like mammals (see MASTODON). Mammoths thrived during the Pleistocene epoch, which began 1.64 million years ago. They probably became extinct at the end of the last ice age, about 10,000 years ago (see ICE AGE; PLEISTOCENE EPOCH).

Mammoths resembled the modern-day elephant. The different species varied in size. The smaller ones were about the size of a modern elephant. Some large mammoths measured 14 ft. [4.3 m] tall at the shoulder. The tusks of some mammoths were 13 ft. [4 m] long.

Mammoths had fur and a thick layer of fat to protect them from the bitter cold of the ice age. The hair of the woolly mammoth was long and shaggy and covered the entire body.

Mammoths lived in Europe, Asia, and North America. They were hunted by prehistoric people, some of whom pictured mammoths in cave drawings. In Siberia, several mammoths were discovered perfectly preserved in ice. Mammoth fossils have also been found in Alaska, Texas, and New York. The reason for the extinction of mammoths is still unknown. *See also* ELEPHANT; EXTINCTION.

MAMMOTH

The mammoth existed in Pleistocene times. Many mammoths have been found whole in frozen soil and glaciers, allowing study of their soft parts and stomach contents.

MANATEE The manatee, sometimes called the sea cow, is a large aquatic mammal (see MAMMAL). The manatee belongs to the order Sirenia. It grows to about 14 ft. [4 m] in length and weighs about 1,500 lb. [680 kg]. The manatee looks something like a walrus or seal. It has light to dark gray skin with short, bristlelike hairs scattered over its body. The manatee has a set of short, paddle-shaped front legs and no hind legs. Its tail is rounded and is used for propulsion.

There are three species of manatee. The West Indian manatee lives in the Caribbean Sea and along the northeastern coast of South America. It is also found in the coastal waters of the southeastern part of the United States, particularly in the bays and rivers of Florida. The Amazonian manatee lives in the Amazon and Orinoco rivers of South America. The African manatee lives in the rivers and coastal waters of western Africa.

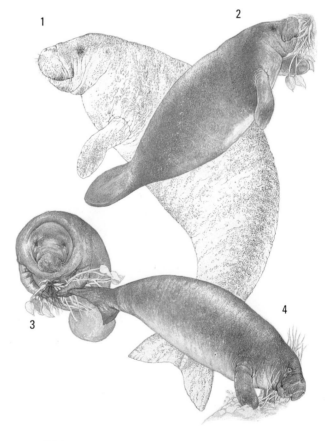

MANATEE

Pictured above are (1) Steller's sea cow, which was hunted to extinction in the 1700s; (2) the Amazonian manatee, which eats floating plants; (3) the West Indian manatee, which carries food in its flippers; and (4) the dugong, which is closely related to the manatee.

The manatee feeds on aquatic plants in fresh or salt water. It can consume about 100 lb. [40 kg] of plants per day. Its upper lip is divided into halves, which close like pliers on plants. Sometimes people place manatees into plant-choked waterways. The manatees eat up the aquatic plants and clear the channel. The West Indian manatee has been heavily hunted for its flesh, hide, and oil. It is now classified as an endangered species.
See also ENDANGERED SPECIES.

MANDRILL The mandrill is a large monkey. It lives in the forests of Cameroon and neighboring parts of western Africa. Mandrills look like baboons, having dark brown fur, long arms, and large canine teeth. The male mandrill is vividly colored. Its cheeks are blue, its nose is red, and its hind end is red and blue. The colors become more brilliant when the animal is excited.

Like most monkeys, mandrills live in groups. They roam about on the ground, feeding mainly on fruits and other plant food.
See also MONKEY.

MANDRILL
The mandrill is a large monkey. The male (shown here) has vivid colors on his face and neck.

MANGO The mango is a large, evergreen tree that thrives in tropical and subtropical areas (see EVERGREEN). It often reaches a height of 60 ft. [18 m]. The narrow leaves are about 1 ft. [30 cm] long and are simple and leathery (see LEAF). The tiny pink or white flowers grow in huge clusters at the ends of small branches.

The mango fruit is usually about the size of an apple, but it may grow to weigh more than 4.4 lb. [2 kg]. Some types of mango fruits are red or yellow with black spots. Other types are dull green. The mango fruit has a soft, juicy pulp that is very sweet. This fruit is a good source of vitamins A, C, and D (see VITAMIN). The mango originated in southern Asia but is now one of the most widely cultivated of the tropical fruits.

MANGROVE Mangroves are dicotyledonous trees, belonging to several families, that grow well in salty ocean swamps, estuaries, and coastal lagoons. A mangrove tree produces hundreds of adventitious roots from the branches (see DICOTYLEDON; ESTUARY; ROOT). These tangled aerial roots tend to catch silt and other debris. This causes the buildup of mud near the tree and helps reclaim land from the sea. However, for the tree to live, the mangrove roots need to be exposed to salt water. Therefore, the buildup of mud may eventually kill the mangrove tree.

The mangrove seed often germinates while it is still on the tree (see GERMINATION). The seed produces a root that may grow 1 ft. [30 cm] long or longer. If this root touches the collected mud near the tree, it begins to grow into a new tree—often while still attached to the parent tree. At other times, when the fruit falls off the tree, the root is driven deep into the mud, anchoring the new plant and enabling it to grow right away. Many mangroves produce breathing roots, called pneumatophores, which rise above the water to get oxygen.

The most common mangrove is the red mangrove. This tree grows from Florida to South America in protected ocean areas along the coasts. It reaches a height of 30 ft. [9 m]. It has leathery leaves that sometimes reach a length of 6 in.

MANGROVE

At low tide, the roots of the trees in a mangrove swamp are exposed. When the tide comes in, the roots provide shelter for fish and mollusks.

[15 cm]. The red mangrove has pale yellow flowers. The bark yields the chemical tannin, which is used in tanning leather.

MANOMETER (mă nŏm′ ĭ tər) A manometer is an instrument used to measure the pressure of gas. There are several types of manometers. The most common type consists of a *U*-shaped tube with both ends open. The tube contains a liquid, often mercury, that fills the bottom of the *U* and rises a short distance in each arm. To measure the pressure of a gas, the open end of one arm is attached to a hose or pipe containing the gas. The other end of the *U* remains open to the atmosphere. In this way, the liquid in the tube is exposed to the pressure of the gas in one arm and to the pressure of the atmosphere in the other arm.

If the pressure of the gas is higher than the pressure of the atmosphere, the liquid rises in the arm of the tube exposed to the air. The difference between the heights of the liquid in both arms is measured to determine the pressure of this amount of liquid. The sum of this pressure and the atmospheric pressure is the pressure of the gas.

Gas pressure is often measured in units of the height of the liquid in the manometer. For example,

gas pressure is often expressed as centimeters of mercury. Normal atmospheric pressure is 76 cm.

In some manometers, the air is removed from one end of the tube, and that end is sealed. This eliminates difficulties caused by variations in atmospheric pressure. The difference between the levels of liquid in the arms shows the pressure of the gas. This type of manometer is usually called a vacuum gauge or pressure gauge.

Some manometers work on the principle of a spring attached to an indicator. The indicator moves in front of a graduated scale that gives direct pressure readings. This type of manometer is called the sphygmomanometer. Doctors use such a gauge to measure people's blood pressure.
See also BAROMETER.

MANTIS Mantises are long, slender insects. There are about 2,000 species. Some scientists place them in the cockroach order (Dictyoptera), while others put them in their own order, Mantodea. They are commonly called "praying mantises." This name refers to their habit of lifting the front legs toward the head, as if in prayer. The mantis takes this position when hunting. When an insect comes within range, the mantis's front legs shoot out at great speed. The prey is trapped in the

mantis's viselike grip. Mantises feed on a wide range of insects, including other mantises.

Mantises are usually found in warm countries, though some species live in the northern regions of the United States and in parts of Canada. Depending on the species, a full-grown mantis ranges from about 2 to 5 in. [5 to 13 cm] in length. The insect's wings are short and broad and folded flat on the back. Most mantises are green or brown and blend in color with the plants on which they live (see CAMOUFLAGE).

Each female mantis lays its eggs in a frothy mass, which sticks to trees and shrubs. The froth hardens as it dries. The young generally hatch in the spring. Mantises often eat other insects that are harmful to people.
See also INSECT.

MANTLE The mantle is the portion of the earth between the crust and the core. The mantle is composed of dense rocks and is 1,800 mi. [2,900 km] thick. The rocks in the mantle are made up of minerals containing aluminum, iron, magnesium, oxygen, and silicon. The

MANTIS

The praying mantis is a skilled hunter. It feeds on many different kinds of insects—including other mantises.

minerals are sometimes forced to the earth's surface through volcanoes (see VOLCANO).

The boundary between the earth's crust and the mantle is called the Mohorovičić Discontinuity, or Moho. On land, the Moho is about 20 mi. [32 km] beneath the surface, but under the oceans, it is only about 5 mi. [8 km] beneath the ocean floor (see MOHO).

The earth's mantle is under great pressure and temperature. The upper mantle, near the Moho, has a temperature of about 1,600°F [870°C]. The lower mantle, near the earth's outer core, has a temperature of about 4,000°F [2,200°C].

Scientists have learned from seismology (the study of earthquakes) that rocks in the upper mantle are plastic, not rigid. Scientists have suggested that the movement of the continents is caused to some degree by the way that the rocks in the mantle move.
See also CONTINENTAL DRIFT; EARTH; LITHOSPHERE AND ASTHENOSPHERE; PLATE TECTONICS.

MAP AND MAPPING

A map is a representation of part or all of the earth on a flat surface or globe. There are many different types of maps, most of which can be placed in one of two main groups: reference maps and special maps.

Reference maps Reference maps portray cities, countries, continents, and bodies of water. A road map is a reference map used by travelers. Other types of transportation maps are used by police and the military. A book of reference maps is called an atlas.

Special maps Special maps emphasize a certain characteristic or feature of an area. For example, a physical map emphasizes the landscape or relief (elevation differences) of an area, either by color, by contour lines, or as a three-dimensional model (see CONTOUR LINE; TOPOGRAPHY). A population map shows different population densities by degrees of shading. A weather map uses symbols to represent weather systems affecting a given area.

Scale Maps are drawn to scale. This means that a given distance on a map equals a certain, larger distance on the earth's surface. A map must be drawn to scale to be accurate.

STATE MAPS

All the U.S. states have been mapped in various ways for different purposes. This map of Washington shows the boundaries of all the counties and the locations of all the county seats.

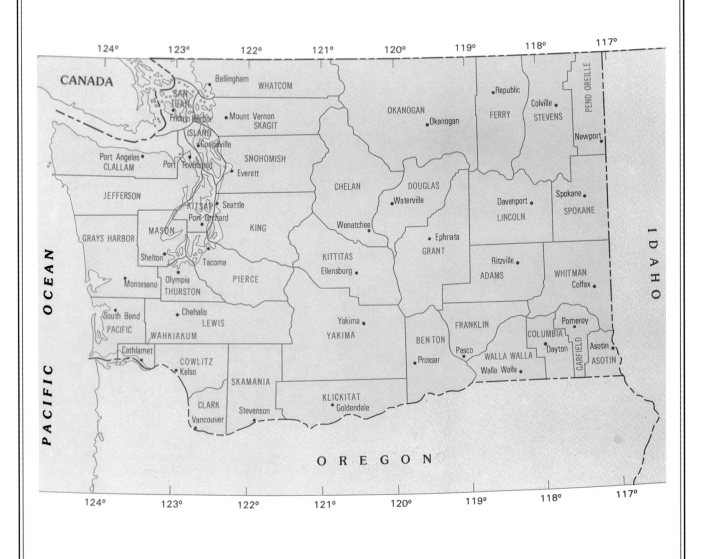

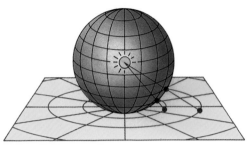

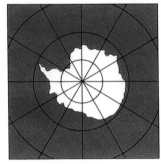

AZIMUTHAL PROJECTION

Azimuthal projections are made by supposing a light source to be in the center of a transparent globe that is touching a piece of paper at only one point. At left, the globe touches the paper at the South Pole. The distortion made by this projection, however, means that distances are increasingly "stretched" farther away from the South Pole.

CONIC PROJECTION

Conic projections are made as if a light in the center of a transparent globe is shining onto a cone of paper placed over the globe. The distances are distorted. The least distortion occurs at the standard parallel, the line where the cone touches the globe. At right is a conic projection of the North Pole.

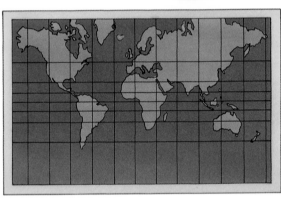

CYLINDRICAL PROJECTION

A cylindrical projection is made as if a light in the center of a transparent globe is shining onto a cylinder of paper wrapped around the globe. At left, the cylinder touches the globe along the equator. The lines of latitude get farther apart nearer the poles.

DISTORTION

(1) The only kind of map that does not make distortions is the globe. The globe is a true representation of the earth. However, only part of the earth can be directly seen at one time. (2) A projection of the globe called an interrupted projection can be made by peeling off the surface of the globe like an orange. This, however, is not very useful as a map. (3) A sinusoidal projection shows the entire world, but this distorts the areas at the top, bottom, right, and left. (4) A Mercator projection results in the areas near the poles appearing larger than they actually are.

1 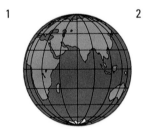 2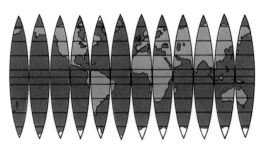

3 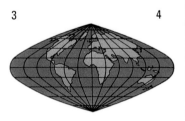 4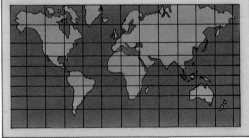

Some maps use an equality to explain the scale, such as 1 in. = 14 mi. This equality means that 1 in. on the map is equal to 14 mi. on the earth's surface. Another way to show a scale is through a ratio or fraction scale, such as 1:60,000 or 1/60,000. The ratio or fraction means that one unit on the map is equal to 60,000 units on the earth's surface. This method of scale is accurate regardless of the system of units used (see FRACTION; RATIO).

Map symbols

Map symbols make a map easier to read. Sometimes these symbols look like what they are representing. For example, a symbol shaped like a cow may represent an area of dairy farming on an agricultural map. A dot is often used to represent a city. The size of the dot may indicate the population of the city. Most maps have legends, or keys, that explain the symbols used on the map.

Lines on a map that link places of equal value are called isolines. Contour lines are isolines that link places of equal altitude, or elevation. Isotherms link places of equal temperature on a weather map (see ISOBAR AND ISOTHERM).

Color

Color is another aid in reading a map. Countries or states are often shown in different colors for contrast. For example, a map of North America may show Canada in green, the United States in yellow, and Mexico in red. These colors make the countries easy to distinguish.

Color may also be used to represent the altitude of a landform. Shading is sometimes used to show differences in rainfall in a given area or to portray population densities.

Finding locations on a map

Latitude and longitude describe locations on a map. Lines of latitude, called parallels, include the equator and the lines parallel to it. Lines of longitude, called meridians, run from the North Pole to the South Pole at right angles to the equator. Knowing the latitude and longitude of a certain place makes it easier to locate on a map (see LATITUDE AND LONGITUDE).

Some maps provide an alphabetical index of places on the map. In the index, each place is followed by a number and a letter. The number corresponds to numbers that run along the top and bottom of the map. The letter corresponds to letters that run along the sides of the map. For example, on a map of the United States, New York City could be located by first looking in the index. If the index says 7H for New York City, then New York City lies approximately where a line drawn from 7 meets a line drawn from H.

The making of a map

The making of a map involves the work of many specially trained people. These people make many observations of the area to be mapped. Measurements of distance, direction, and elevation are taken. Aerial

MAPPING INSTRUMENTS

Cartographers use various scientific instruments, such as the calibrated eyepiece shown here, to make sure that the drawing of a map is accurate.

photographs (photographs taken from the air) are studied and interpreted.

Many scientific instruments are used to make a map. A theodolite measures horizontal and vertical angles over a long distance. By using this device, mapmakers can determine distances from one point to another. A tellurometer determines distances by measuring the time it takes radio waves to travel between two points. Another instrument determines distance by measuring how long it takes light waves to travel between two points. A level is a device used to measure elevation. A clinometer is used to measure the angle of elevation between two points.

Aerial photography has come into wide use for mapping since World War II (1939–1945). Aerial photographs show tremendous detail and help in the mapping of rugged mountain areas. Photogrammetry is the science of making measurements from aerial photographs. Mapmakers also use satellite images of land and water areas. A satellite that orbits the earth records information from the heat and light reflected from the earth's surface. The information is sent back to earth and converted to an image that looks like a color photograph. Large areas of the earth's surface can be recorded this way.

When all the observations have been completed and analyzed, a cartographer (mapmaker) organizes the data into a map plan. From this plan, the cartographer incorporates the data into an accurate, easy-to-read map.

Map projections

The only type of map that can be completely accurate is a global map. A globe shows locations, shapes, and distances correctly, because it, like the earth, is round. Unfortunately, a globe is clumsy to carry around, and only one part of a globe can be observed at a time. Therefore, cartographers have devised map projections, which are flat maps. Different types of projections are used for different types of maps. Each type of projection has advantages and disadvantages.

An azimuthal projection projects the surface of a globe on a flat surface that touches the globe at only one point. This type of projection is the easiest to make, but it results in distortion of distance.

A conic projection projects an area of the earth's surface on a cone of paper placed over the globe. Again, some distortion of distance occurs.

A cylindrical projection projects the earth's surface on a piece of paper wrapped around a globe. This results in a map where all the meridians are at right angles to the parallels. On a cylindrical projection, however, the extreme north and south polar areas have distorted distances.

Some projections, called conventional projections, are variations of a global map of the world. Conventional projections include sinusoidal, interrupted, and Mercator projections.

COMPUTER MAPPING
Modern computer-based systems have helped speed up mapmaking processes and improved the accuracy of today's maps.

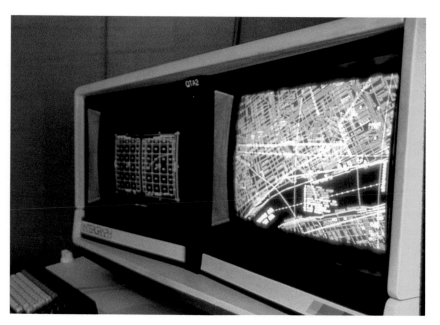

MAPLE FAMILY

The sugary sap of the rock maple is made into maple syrup.

MAPLE FAMILY The maple family includes about 200 species of trees growing in the northern temperate zones of the world. There are 13 species of maples native to the United States. The large, flat leaves are usually divided into three to seven lobes (see LEAF). The flowers are small and greenish, with four or five petals. The seeds usually grow in pairs and are enclosed in dry, flat, winglike fruits called keys (see DISPERSION OF PLANTS).

Maples are valued as shade trees and for the color they add to the autumn landscape. Some types of maples have great commercial value. One such maple is the rock maple, native to North America. It is also called the sugar maple or the hard maple. The wood of the rock maple is light, reddish brown, and very hard and strong, making it valuable as lumber. This tree also yields a sugary sap that can be processed into maple syrup, maple sugar, and other products.

The maple leaf is the national emblem of Canada, and it appears on the Canadian flag. Other members of the maple family common in North America include the silver maple, the Japanese maple, and the box elder.

MARBLE Marble is a type of hard limestone that can be polished to a high gloss. It is formed from limestone that has been metamorphosed (changed) by the tremendous heat and pressure beneath the earth's surface. Unmetamorphosed limestones that can take a polish are sometimes called marbles, too (see LIMESTONE; METAMORPHIC ROCK). The limestone becomes a hard, crystalline rock without cavities and holes. The crystals that make up pure marble are of the minerals calcite and dolomite (see CRYSTAL; MINERAL). Pure marble is snow white. Colored and banded marble contain various impurities, including such minerals as graphite and iron.

Marble was used in ancient times for statues and

MARBLE—Use in buildings

The famous Taj Mahal, an ornate tomb built by a Mogul emperor in Agra, India, is made of white marble.

MARBLE—Decoration
The surface of marble can be decorated with fancy inlays as pictured above.

fine buildings. The quarries of Carrara, Italy, are known for their high-quality marble. Famous sculptors, including Michelangelo and Leonardo da Vinci, used this marble for many of their works. In the United States, the largest marble quarry is located in Vermont.

MARCONI, GUGLIELMO (1874–1937)
(mär kō′ nē, g͞oo lyĕl′ mô) Guglielmo Marconi was an Italian electrical engineer known for inventing the radio (see RADIO). Radio waves were discovered in 1887 by Heinrich Hertz (see ELECTROMAGNETIC RADIATION; HERTZ, HEINRICH). Marconi had the idea that these waves could be used to carry messages. At that time, messages were already being sent using electric wires by means of Samuel Morse's telegraph (see MORSE, SAMUEL FINLEY BREESE; TELEGRAPH). Marconi wanted to develop a way to transmit information long distances without having to rely on miles of electrical wires.

After working on the problem for some time, Marconi produced an electric bell that could be rung from 30 ft. [9.3 m] away. The bell was switched on by an electrical pulse that was carried through the air by radio waves. By 1895, Marconi had developed equipment capable of transmitting pulses as far as a mile.

The Italian government showed little interest in supporting Marconi's work. Marconi decided to try his luck in England. The British government was very helpful and granted him a patent for his device. With this patent, Marconi was able to start the Marconi Company in 1897. Two years later, he transmitted a radio signal across the English Channel. On December 12, 1901, he used his equipment to send a message across the Atlantic Ocean, from England to Newfoundland. Marconi went on experimenting and improving radio transmission all his life. For his work, he was awarded the Nobel Prize for physics in 1909.

MARIJUANA (măr′ ə wä′ nə) Marijuana is an illegal drug derived from the leaves and flowers of the hemp plant (*Cannabis sativa*) (see DRUG; HEMP). The hemp plant grows naturally in many parts of the world, including the United States. It is also cultivated illegally for sale in many countries. The active ingredient in marijuana is tetrahydrocannabinol (THC). Because the amount of THC varies from plant to plant, the strength of marijuana also varies. Marijuana is usually rolled into a cigarette and smoked, though it may be put into foods or beverages and eaten or drunk.

Marijuana was not always illegal. It had been used for thousands of years as an intoxicant and a medicine. In 1937, the United States outlawed the possession, use, and sale of marijuana. Relatively few people used the drug at the time, so there was little controversy over the law. However, in the 1960s, the use of marijuana increased greatly, and so did the controversy over the law. A special government group was appointed to study the problems of marijuana use and to make recommendations to the president. In 1972, the group recommended that criminal penalties for the private possession and use of marijuana be done away with. They also recommended that the sale of the drug remain illegal. The federal government and many state governments reduced the criminal charge of possession of small amounts of marijuana from a felony to a misdemeanor. A felony is a crime in which punishment is a jail sentence of more than one year. A misdemeanor is a crime in which punishment is a shorter jail sentence or a fine. Some states have substituted fines for jail sentences altogether.

The effects of smoking marijuana may last for as long as five hours. Eating marijuana may produce effects for twelve hours. The effects of marijuana vary and depend on the strength of the marijuana, the amount used, the setting in which it is used, and the experience of the user. There is usually a false sense of happiness and well-being while using the drug. Sometimes, there may be a feeling of panic. When the drug is used in large amounts, there may be some distortion of vision and of the person's sense of space and time. Minutes may seem like hours, and short distances may seem to be much longer. Marijuana causes several immediate physical effects, such as reddening of the eyes, increased heart rate, decreased blood pressure, and increased appetite.

There is controversy over the long-term effects of marijuana. Some people believe that marijuana use leads to the use of narcotics, such as heroin. However, there is no scientific proof that this is true (see NARCOTIC). Smoking marijuana can be as harmful to the lungs as smoking tobacco, however (see TOBACCO). Pregnant women who use marijuana may have babies that are born prematurely. Frequent use of marijuana has not been found to cause addiction. However, it can cause psychological

dependence. Also, marijuana is often used with other drugs that can be addicting, such as alcohol (see ADDICTION; ALCOHOLISM).

Scientists have found that marijuana may be useful in treating certain disorders such as glaucoma and chronic pain and in controlling the nausea brought on by certain cancer treatment medications (see CANCER; GLAUCOMA; PAIN). In 1980, the U.S. Food and Drug Administration (FDA) approved the limited medical use of pills that contain THC. The FDA has also approved a tightly regulated program that is studying how smoking marijuana affects certain cancer and glaucoma patients.

Hashish, or hash, is also derived from the hemp plant. It is a much stronger drug than marijuana. Hashish is produced from the resins of the plant. *See also* RESIN.

MARINE BIOLOGY Marine biology is the study of living things in the oceans. The word *marine* refers to the ocean. Scientists who study marine biology are called marine biologists. They study microscopic organisms, seaweed, clams, lobsters, fish, birds, mammals, and other organisms that live in or around the oceans. Today, people are

MARINE BIOLOGY

Marine biologists study all the creatures that live in the sea, including those that are attached to the sea bed. Most bottom-dwellers are simple organisms, some of which are shown right.

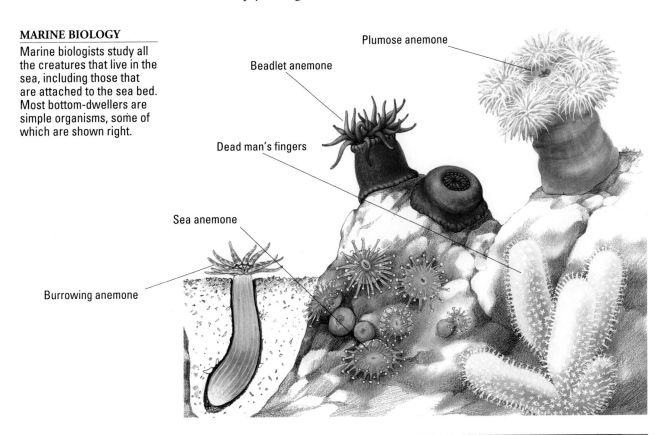

Plumose anemone

Beadlet anemone

Dead man's fingers

Sea anemone

Burrowing anemone

turning to the sea to obtain more energy, food, water, and minerals. Marine biologists are becoming more important because of their knowledge of the ocean and its resources.
See also OCEANOGRAPHY.

MARMOSET (mär′ mə sĕt′) The marmosets are among the smallest monkeys (see MONKEY). They live in the forests of Panama and South America. Marmosets are usually less than 1 ft. [30 cm] in length, not including the tail. Most weigh less than 1 lb. [0.5 kg]. The tails of most marmosets are longer than their bodies. Unlike many other monkeys of South America, the marmoset's tail is never prehensile (used for grasping). Marmosets have claws instead of nails like other monkeys. The larger species of marmosets are also called tamarins.

Some marmosets have tufts of hair above their ears. Some have beards or mustaches. The golden or lion-headed marmoset has soft, golden hair that resembles a lion's mane. Marmosets live in groups, moving from tree to tree like squirrels. These monkeys move about only during the day. At night, they sleep in trees. Marmosets feed mainly on fruits and insects.

MARMOSET
The strikingly colored golden marmoset lives in the forests of South America.

Many marmosets have been captured to be sold as pets. The rain forests, where marmosets live, are also being destroyed at a rapid pace. Therefore, many species of marmosets, including the golden marmoset, have become endangered.
See also ENDANGERED SPECIES; RAIN FOREST.

MARMOT The marmot, a rodent, is the largest member of the squirrel family (see RODENT; SQUIRREL). There are various kinds of marmots. Most live in mountainous regions in North America and Europe and in much of Asia.

MARMOT
When an Alpine marmot spots a wolf, it stands up and whistles an alarm.

Marmots living in North America range from about 1 to 2 ft. [30 to 61 cm] in length, not including the tail. These animals have short legs, small ears, and furry tails. Most marmots have gray fur on their backs, with reddish or yellowish orange fur covering their bellies. Marmots feed on grasses and other plants. These animals hibernate in burrows during the winter (see HIBERNATION). The groundhog, also called the woodchuck, is a kind of marmot that lives in fields and woods of the eastern United States.
See also PRAIRIE DOG.

Mars is the fourth planet from the sun. It is the earth's second closest neighbor after Venus. At its closest, Mars passes within 35 million mi. [56 million km] of the earth.

Mars has a diameter of 4,200 mi. [6,760 km], which is about half the diameter of the earth. It takes Mars 687 days to make a complete orbit, or rotation, around the sun. A Martian day lasts 24 hours and 37 minutes, slightly longer than an Earth day. The distance between the sun and Mars averages 141.5 million mi. [227.7 million km].

Mars is much colder than the earth. The average temperature on Mars is about -80°F [-62°C]. At night, the temperature may drop to -150°F [-101°C]. Mars's axis (the invisible line running through its center, from pole to pole) has a tilt of about 25°. This tilt is responsible for the Martian seasons, just as on Earth (see SEASON). Scientists think that the summer daytime temperature at the Martian equator reaches 70°F [21 °C].

VIKING VIEW

This is the view of Mars taken by one of the *Viking* space probes as it approached the planet in preparation for landing.

The surface of Mars When viewed through a telescope, Mars seems to be made up of bright areas and dark areas. These areas constantly change shape. The bright areas, which cover about two-thirds of Mars, are reddish brown deserts. Scientists think that the deserts may contain limonite, a mineral that is also found in deserts on Earth.

The dark areas are called maria, or seas, even though they contain no water. The maria seem to become greenish during the Martian spring and summer. During the Martian autumn and winter, the maria appear bluish gray, and some maria disappear completely. Astronomers think that these variations may be caused by the blowing and settling of dust and sand.

Through the centuries, many observers have seen lines on the surface of Mars. These lines have come to be called canals. However, these so-called canals do not show up in any of the thousands of photographs of the Martian surface taken by space probes (see SPACE EXPLORATION). Instead, the photographs show irregular channels resembling dried-up riverbeds. For this reason, most astronomers

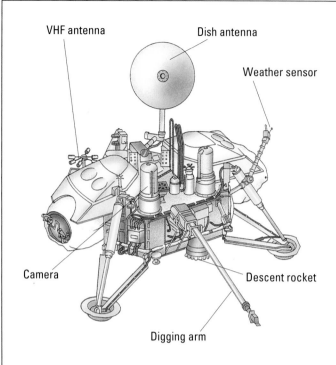

VHF antenna

Dish antenna

Weather sensor

Camera

Descent rocket

Digging arm

VIKING LANDER

The *Viking* probes had automatic soil samplers. They tested the Martian soil for traces of life, but did not find any. The weather sensor detected winds of up to 75 m.p.h. [120 kph].

have concluded that the canals are an optical illusion and do not exist on the surface of Mars.

Photographs show that the southern hemisphere of Mars is heavily cratered. The northern hemisphere, on the other hand, is the site of some of the largest volcanoes in the solar system. The north and south poles of Mars are covered by white polar caps. These polar caps are composed of both solid

MARTIAN SURFACE

Cameras on the *Viking* lander showed the surface of Mars to be a waterless desert with many scattered boulders.

carbon dioxide (dry ice) and frozen water. The polar caps expand during the winter and contract (become smaller) during the summer.

The Martian atmosphere is much thinner than the earth's atmosphere. The atmosphere of Mars contains 1 to 2 percent argon, 2 to 3 percent nitrogen, 95 percent carbon dioxide, and 0.3 percent oxygen. There is also a very small amount of water vapor in the air. The Martian atmosphere has about 1 percent the density of the earth's atmosphere. This accounts for the vast temperature changes on the surface of Mars. Occasionally, thick clouds, possibly made of water vapor, drift across the planet.

The moons of Mars Mars has two small satellites, or moons. Phobos, the larger moon, has a diameter of 14 mi. [23 km]. It makes a complete orbit around Mars every $7^1/_2$ hours. The smaller moon, Deimos, takes 30 hours to orbit Mars. The diameter of Deimos is 6 mi. [10 km]. Both moons were discovered by the American astronomer Asaph Hall in 1877.

Space probes to Mars Several unmanned space probes have studied Mars. Four American space probes—*Mariner IV, Mariner VI, Mariner VII,* and *Mariner IX*—all visited but did not land on Mars. These probes sent photographs of the Martian moons, dust storms, and the previously unknown Martian craters back to Earth.

In 1976, the American *Viking I* and *Viking II* space probes landed on the Martian surface. They transmitted superb photographs of the Martian landscape. *Viking I* and *Viking II* also analyzed the soil and atmosphere of Mars. None of the space probes have detected any evidence of life on Mars.

The *Mars Observer* space probe, launched in 1992, was expected to provide more detailed information about the surface, gravitational field, and atmosphere of Mars. However, in 1993, just before the probe was to begin orbiting the planet, scientists permanently lost contact with it. They believe that a leak in the spacecraft's fuel system caused it to spin out of control and lose power.

See also EXOBIOLOGY; PLANET; SOLAR SYSTEM.